HEAL[...]
THROU[...]
EARTH EN[...]

To [...] John, with best wishes for your own healing p[...]
Judy Jacka

JUDY JACKA is best known for her work with natural therapies in which she has consulted, lectured, written and taught for over twenty-five years. She also has a life-long interest in the metaphysical teaching of Blavatsky and Bailey, and is a senior worker in the Arcane school. Her esoteric interests have been expressed through writing and teaching about subtle forms of healing.

In this book, Judy Jacka has integrated the Vivaxis teachings and information about earth energies with her long experience of other natural therapies and the ancient wisdom teachings about our subtle energies. She has succeeded in making a working synthesis of many aspects of earth energies.

Judy has taught the Vivaxis techniques in this book since 1980 in Australia, New Zealand, Canada and Europe.

ACKNOWLEDGEMENTS

Because of the unusual and complex nature of this topic, *Healing through Earth Energies* has been the most difficult to write of my five published books. I am particularly grateful to my dear friends Jenny Coller, Sheryl Callanan and Michael Beatrice for reading and giving feedback on the original manuscript. My thanks also to Deenne Pettipas of the Vivaxis Energies Research International Society in Canada who supplied me with some valuable material from the early writings of Fran Nixon. And last but not least, my thanks to the many students of Vivaxis who over the last fifteen years have proved to me that the exercises in the book are particularly relevant and meaningful in our daily life.

Thomas C. Lothian Pty Ltd
11 Munro Street, Port Melbourne, Victoria 3207

Copyright © Judy Jacka 1996
First published 1996

National Library of Australia
Cataloguing-in-Publication data:

Jacka, Judy.
    Healing through earth energies.

    Includes index.
    ISBN 0 85091 783 2.

    1. Healing. 2. Nature, Healing power of.
    3. Earth – Health aspects. I. Title.

615.53

Cover and text design by Stanley Wong
Cover illustration by Susie Parry
Text illustrations by Julia McLeish
Typeset by The Imagemaking Centre, South Melbourne, Victoria
Printed in Australia by McPherson's Printing Group

HEALING
THROUGH
EARTH ENERGIES

Judy Jacka

Lothian
B O O K S

This book is dedicated to the memory of Frances Nixon who was a true pioneer of the healing energies available from planet Earth.

Other books by this author

A-Z of Natural Therapies
Meditation, the Most Natural Therapy
Philosophy of Healing
Frontiers of Natural Therapies

FOREWORD

My first encounter with the topic of 'Vivaxis' was via personal contact with Fran Nixon in the late 1960s/early 1970s. We became friends as I tried to understand her descriptions and explanations of the craft. I felt that, since I was in the process of developing a multidimensional model of the universe that discriminated between physical, etheric, emotional, mental and spiritual substances and radiations, I should be able to describe how the process worked. Although I made mention of Vivaxis in a couple of the papers written in the 1970s, I never did intellectually penetrate the topic to a satisfactory level and thus left it alone until some new insight might appear in my consciousness that would allow me to see an internally self-consistent explanation of the wide variety of phenomena involved.

I now think that learning to develop and trust the dowsing response in oneself is extremely important at this point in human history. It opens our access to vast information and energy fields, present and available in the universe, that heretofore were blocked for most of us because they are detectable presently only at subliminal levels.

Although the dowsing response is most well known in the area of water detection, it can be utilised to enhance one's situation in any area – medicine, science, engineering, business, human relations, etc. To gain this enhanced intuition, it is necessary to practise just like for any other type of learning or muscle development. (But this is supervised neural learning.) However, it is first necessary to adjust one's mindset to allow – and even encourage – this subliminal signal transfer from one's unconscious level processing to the conscious awareness state.

Careful research on a water dowser, who is also very sensitive to various forms of electromagnetic energy, has shown that the adrenal glands (and perhaps the pituitary gland) are implicated as body sensors. Canadian research has shown that the upper arm muscles electrically fire an instant before the dowsing wand twitches downwards to indicate the presence of water.

Ordinary neural signals play no role in dowsing. Rather, it is subliminal information, picked up by the body's sense organs and registered in the 'old' brain, that leads to the dowsing response via modulation of involuntary muscle activity.

Interestingly, the human body appears to have two essentially parallel sets of nerve fibres extending from the sensory organs to the brain. Along one set, rapidly moving trains of signals of relatively large amplitude travel to the cerebral cortex for registration. This leads to conscious perception of the information content inherent in the sensory signals. Along the other set of nerve fibres, slowly moving trains of signals of subliminal amplitude travel to the brainstem (the old 'reptilian' or 'instinctive' brain) and to the reticular network in the mid-brain location between the left and right hemispheres of the cerebral cortex.

This old brainstem is the seat of the primary thought processes of unconscious activity that controls involuntary muscle movement such as breathing, heartbeat, pupil size, genital erections, etc. Conscious processes are labelled secondary thought processes because they involve higher order processing in the cerebral cortex. During the sleep state, when the cerebral cortex has raised its neural firing threshold for consciousness so that the system will not be disturbed easily, it is the nerve signals from the reticular network that can automatically lower this firing threshold and produce wakefulness when the instinctive brain senses the need.

When an entity is born into the physical domain at a particular point in space-time, all the relative planetary positions of the various celestial bodies are precisely set. This specific map of physical substance in space-time has a conjugate map of etheric substance in the frequency domain via the Fourier Transform process. Likewise, the being enters life with a specific signature located in a well-defined region of the frequency domain (etheric domain). Some type of local magnetic polarisation can be expected to occur in this etheric domain when 'life' (entrance of some spirit into the fetus) for this entity begins. I would like to define that unique polarisation field and the frequency domain as the individual's Vivaxis which remains at that location while the individual's physical body grows and moves from place to place in space; the companion etheric body also grows and shifts from one region of the frequency domain to another. It is the various magnetoelectric radiations from the many planetary aspects configured in the frequency domain that interact with the magnetic aspects of the entity's etheric body and create both positive and negative effects on the individual.

Within the framework of my multidimensional model, a basis exists for rationalising the existence of a unique Vivaxis field at the etheric level of substance (whose four coordinate of cognitive description are all frequencies) for all individuals. Likewise the 'stuff' and procedures of the Vivaxis techniques seem to deal with the magnetic monopole counterparts of electric monopole substance at the physical level as well as the magnetoelectric radiation counterpart of the electromagnetic radiations involved with this physical substance. The fine details of this correspondence remain to be worked out in quantitative detail. Hopefully, the contents of this book by Judy Jacka will motivate some scientist to do that in the not-too-distant future.

William A. Tiller
PROFESSOR EMERITUS

Department of Materials Science and Engineering
Stanford University

CONTENTS

INTRODUCTION

Seventeen years ago I was introduced to earth energies by the late Frances Nixon from Canada. At the time I had no idea what an adventure was to unfold. With hindsight, I can now say that my study of earth energies remains the most amazing aspect of health and healing I have encountered among those therapies studied, practised and taught by me over a thirty-year period.

The story begins when I was introduced to Fran's discoveries by an Australian chiropractor who had attended one of her Canadian seminars and subsequently supplied me with some reading matter. During this time, in the mid-seventies, I was developing the Southern School of Natural Therapies and lecturing on naturopathic philosophy and the principles of natural therapies. A major aim of mine was to build a bridge between energy as understood by orthodox science and the vitalistic concept of natural therapies. The keystone or foundation of natural therapy is restoring and balancing the energies of the body, and I was always on the lookout for scientific material on the subject of vitality to present to students.

From studying the work of Fran, I was impressed that she had secured the interest of several physicists in Canada and the USA.[1] She followed a meticulous routine of checking and rechecking all her material before publishing, or teaching people about her discoveries. The nature of her work convinced me that she was dealing with those subtle energies which are increasingly viewed as providing the blueprint for growth and regrowth or healing.

The other impressive aspect of her work was that she taught people to research their own energies and thus helped them take complete responsibility for their own health, albeit with considerable guidance in the preliminary stage. There were no expensive tests or remedies, or dependence on a therapist – everything in Fran's approach to health was obtained from mother Earth.

In 1979, I wrote to Fran and asked if she would be prepared to do a workshop in Australia. She was delighted to accept and came for two months during which time she conducted a two-week seminar on our property at Kinglake in the Great Dividing Range north of Melbourne. Only ten people showed interest in attending this seminar but later, when I described this work in a leading health journal, I had more letters and enquiries about the subject than from any of my previous books and articles on health and healing.

For the last fifteen years, I have taught small groups the science which Fran shared and which she named the science of Vivaxis. Vivaxis means the axis of life. Before she died in August 1985, I assisted Fran with work in Canada and she asked me to be the one to carry on her work. Fran was a purist, whereas my interest in the healing arts is quite eclectic so I have always combined an interest in earth energies with other aspects of health and healing. Hence this book is not just about the science of Vivaxis, but includes other findings about earth energies and the relationship of earth energies to many aspects of health and healing.

The main aim of this book is to train you to use your own subtle energy body as the instrument for finding, comparing, assessing and using energies. The level at which we will practise is at present beyond the capacity of technology and instruments of physics to measure and may remain so. However, the energies described are still in the physical realm and appear to be closely related to the laws of gravitation, magnetism, and electricity as manifested on this planet. This is why instruments of physics can indirectly measure subtle energies via the electromagnetic field which surrounds and interpenetrates all living beings.

We need to be able to clearly distinguish this energy, subjective as it is at present, from the psychic energy which operates in the astral realm. For this reason, I have included sections in the first few chapters on our subtle constitution and the chakras. It must never be forgotten that the astral realm is that of human desire which can, together with our mental conditioning, influence our work at the more subtle physical level. This has already been demonstrated by science; the observer is now known to influence the observable.

One faculty we use in sensing energies is related to the ancient technique of dowsing, sometimes called the radiesthetic or kinesthetic sense and we explore this ability early in the book. In studying the subject of dowsing, I became aware of previous research related to the finding of various substances under the surface of the planet such as water and mineral deposits. The field of dowsing extends into the area of radionics where practitioners use this subtle sense to diagnose disease and 'broadcast' healing frequencies. We look at this area as an aid to understanding the subject of human vibrations and frequencies.

While working with Vivaxis energies, I became aware of other types of earth energies including ley lines and the Hartmann and Curry grids. I found that these areas have already been somewhat explored by European dowsers and we discuss them in the final two chapters.

Each chapter in this book contains practical exercises so that you can make the book a living experience. I am aware that these exercises may at first glance seem very strange and perhaps even outlandish. But I can promise the earnest student that they will be richly repaid for the time and effort taken to understand and practise this energy work. Another aim in this book is to promote an understanding of the living earth so that we can make use of the energies available. Understanding this subject will also encourage individuals and groups to prevent further destruction of our planet.

I make no apology for the fact that the bulk of the book is devoted to the discoveries of Fran Nixon. In conjunction with the writing stage I have reviewed all her self-published work and continue to be astounded by the implications and applications of her findings. While there are a number of publications on different aspects of earth energies such as Feng Shui and ley lines, none of these works is based on a system which minutely diagnoses and corrects the relationship between the individual and the earth.

The closest parallel would be the traditional Chinese medical system encompassing the five element theory and associated concordances. This system allows us to rebalance our energies through choosing particular food, sounds, colours and surroundings according to our constitution. The Ayurvedic medicine from India also selects food and remedies according to body type and temperament.

However, in the discoveries of Fran Nixon, we have a system of diagnosis and treatment which allows each individual to find and correct energy variations from the gross to the most subtle energy disturbances including disturbances in the individual energy receptors or acupuncture points.

I have often wondered why Fran's extraordinary discoveries

have not been more widely spread. There appears to be another reason apart from the fact that Fran was far before her time and only self-published. The main focus of the New Age movement has been on psychic phenomena and hence on astral or psychic experience. We see this trend in the emphasis on rebirthing in its various forms, past life experiences, promoting bliss experiences, aura readings, and astrological or tarot readings. There have been few individuals or groups who have endeavoured to focus on subtle physical energies. These energies are intrinsic to our health and well-being because they condition our physical bodies.

My training in the Trans-Himalayan teachings transmitted by Blavatsky and Bailey, together with training in the natural healing arts and sciences, attracts me to these subtle physical energies, increasingly known in the West as etheric energies. The more subtle part of our physical body consists of these energies. Fran Nixon used this term herself and explored these energies throughout her career. The etheric world forms an interface between our physical brain consciousness and our different levels of consciousness. We cannot transmit these subtle states or be a reliable instrument unless our etheric body and its associated electromagnetic field is balanced and in order.

The chapters in the book are planned so as to be sequential in the most meaningful way although it is inevitable that some exercises will depend on information in later chapters for their completeness. For instance, in the first chapter the exercise dealing with clearing our circuits is more potent when it is done using the energy layers which in turn may not be found accurately until our circuits are cleared. This is why it has in the past seemed preferable to work with a trained instructor for these early exercises. However, it is time to present this work in more detail and particular care has been taken to spell out the exercises in a way which can be followed independently.

The clearing exercises prepare us to find particular compass directions for elements. We know of more than twenty common elements which have vibrational frequencies and energy flows that can be traced to a particular compass direction. This introduces the whole concept of the vibrational aspect of the universe and natural therapies. We explore the basic testing procedures for energies both within and without the body. We learn about the rhythms and tides produced on our planet by other heavenly bodies, and the techniques we can use for charting some of these interactions. The effect of these various tides and rhythms on our health is significant.

We look at the frequencies and vibrations of many of the key elements which make up our bodies and which need to be balanced for health. I describe techniques for finding and assessing these important elements. This leads to perhaps the key adventure of the book – how to find and use the energy layers on the earth which contain all the frequencies necessary for life.

After we learn to mark the energy layers, we are in a position to find and use our Vivaxis. Our Vivaxis is located at a particular point on the planet and connects us with health-giving frequencies throughout our life. The inherent skills we use to find the energy layers and our Vivaxis relate to the magnetic properties of the pineal gland. Understanding this connection helps us understand the link between our energy centres and the energy layers – this latter work being developed by myself in recent years.

I have included many practical exercises for diagnosing and improving our health including purification of food and water, and guidelines for practitioners and therapists when assessing clients and their needs. For individuals who have extreme energy confusion in their bodies I indicate how to create a new Vivaxis.

Finally, we look at planet Earth and the larger energy channels called ley lines. I discuss the work of Bruce Cathie who made important scientific and mathematical discoveries about these lines. Dowsing and exploring earth and body energies enables us to explore the environment also in terms of what is harmful. In the final chapter of the book I explain how we can check for geopathic stress which is pathology of the earth and to evaluate homes and offices for what is called the sick building syndrome. Some techniques are described to resolve this type of earth and building sickness, including disturbances which are naturally-occurring and those disturbances which are man-made.

This book is just the beginning of a science which is far ahead of mainstream natural therapies, dealing as it does with the source of those vibrational frequencies which form the basis of all natural therapies. It is true pioneering work and must be approached with care and discrimination as should all new therapies.

There may be times in the future when humanity will be completely thrown back on its own resources for health and healing with nothing but the ground we stand on. We will then rejoice that we can use mother Earth for healing and preserving the vehicles for our life or spirit. For our spirit will eventually return to higher realms but our body is indeed a child of, and dependent on, what our planet can provide.

1 RELATING TO EARTH AS A LIVING BEING

★ ★ ★ ★ ★ ★

WHAT do we mean when we use the term earth energies? Are we talking about the known energies of the atom and molecule or more subtle energies? How do we relate earth energies to energy as known by science? Do we ignore science and look at planet Earth as the body of a great consciousness who is evolving towards perfection? Is it possible to make a synthesis of all these factors?

It is only recently that a sizeable group of people in the Western world has accepted that humans have an energy field which radiates around them affecting the environment in a positive or negative sense according to the energies involved. Extending this concept to our planet provides a thought-provoking model of our relation to this globe. This model works from the universal to the particular and views the earth on a parallel with our growing understanding of the human being. From this model we can perceive that there may be similarities in both energy and consciousness between the macrocosm (earth) and the microcosm (the human being).

The concept of mother earth is found in many great religions. In ancient Greece she was known as Gaia and this name was revived by the scientist Sir James Lovelock in his useful book *Gaia – A New Look at Life on Earth*, first published in 1979. Lovelock has a scientific background and a visionary sense which presents life on earth in a new framework – where humanity is a co-creator.

Like a true poet, he manages to encapsulate a view of earth from many perspectives in the space of a small book. The book provides a synthesis of science and insight into the self-balancing and regulating or homeostatic mechanism of our planet. He shows that this mechanism still works despite what we see as the appalling interference by man, but he also warns that this balance could be overturned if humanity does not curb its ecological interference in the future.

Lovelock describes the earth's living matter, oceans, and land surface as a complex system which can also be seen as a single organism that has the capacity to keep our planet a suitable place for life.[1] The impression he gives is that earth could indeed be viewed as a living being. This viewpoint of Gaia suggests that we can see the physical body of our planet in much the same way as a human physical body. Lovelock sees the possibility of humanity becoming the nervous system of the living earth in a meaningful way and acting almost as an outpost of her consciousness. This concept has interesting ramifications for the practical work in this book as we explore the energetic relationships between the human energy field and that of the earth.

The idea of the earth as a living being has also come to us through various mystery schools and religions and was brought to the West from beyond the Himalayas by writers such as Blavatsky and Bailey. The Trans-Himalayan teachings take the Gaia concept further to an understanding that the eco-systems and kingdoms of nature on planet Earth are simply the physical body of a great conscious Being, or Being in whom we live and move and have our being. According to the Bailey teachings, human beings are considered to be living cells in the body of this greater Being in both a physical and spiritual sense.[2]

This consciousness associated with planet Earth is a rational explanation for a Being who is both a transcendent and immanent God who is evolving towards increasing perfection. The ancient wisdom is concerned with the big picture of how all the kingdoms in nature interact and evolve on our planet. In this view, the various kingdoms are all evolving towards perfection and there is a natural Hierarchy of Being and an orderly interaction of eco-systems which form the physical vehicles for many ascending levels of consciousness.

We tend to reject the idea of Hierarchy because we project our human tendency to control others on to this concept. In the ancient wisdom tradition, the Hierarchy is understood to be the result of the natural movement of spirit towards matter and then its return to the source of all being, bearing with it the rewards and qualities developed in the long journey through millions of years. From this viewpoint, the individual human sense of awareness and consciousness is at no time lost but continually grows and expands on its journey back to the source.

We can summarise this teaching as a basic equation which is spirit + matter —> consciousness. Spirit is understood to have chosen to further its expansion by incarnating in planetary substance so as to redeem or reveal the light at the centre of every atom of matter. The human spirits are considered as having their origin in those great Beings whose consciousness uses the various planetary spheres in a way corresponding to how the human spirit uses the physical body as a means of living on the physical plane. The planets including earth revolve around a physical and spiritual centre which we already know as the sun, the centre of our solar system. This is why in many religions the sun is the symbol for the highest spiritual being.

Obviously, there cannot be a sudden jump from spirit to matter (although fundamentally religious people have no trouble with such logic). It is suggested that spirit gradually involutes towards matter through many planes or levels during millions of years and then gradually evolves via the various kingdoms in nature to a position where self-consciousness, and finally spiritual consciousness takes place. It is at the stage of self-consciousness that our truly human journey begins, and perhaps we only know the last million years of this growth on our planet which may have started much earlier.

There are writers in the Western world outside the more esoteric tradition who have also developed comprehensive models of the kingdoms on planet earth. A view of evolution drawing on anthropology, psychology, mythology and religion has been developed by Ken Wilbur in his acclaimed book *Up From Eden*.[3]

The ancient wisdom has emerged through many religions and schools of thought. It further views humanity as part of a vast planetary Hierarchy of Being which stretches from the atom to the Godhead. The teaching encompasses a concept of interacting energy fields at many levels of consciousness. Modern physics has helped this concept at the physical level by recognising the energetic relationships between all atoms and forms on our planet. Our planetary manifestation is seen by some thinkers as a vast thought or hologram rather than as a machine with separate parts.

There is an emphasis on energy fields at both the macrocosmic or microcosmic level.

The energy body is often known as our etheric vehicle and most of the techniques described in this book are dealing with etheric energy. Because the etheric field is conditioned by more subtle fields of emotion and thought it is essential to see the larger picture. Many health problems of the etheric body have their cause in emotional problems and this needs to be underlined before we look at the details of restoring our etheric energy field.

With the broad view of evolution in mind, yet recognising our physical base as within the planet, we now start to consider the practicalities of earth healing, and how we diagnose and use techniques involving planetary energies for healing purposes. Because there are so many energies in the universe at different levels, we need to theorise a little more in order to clearly distinguish the type of energy featured in this book. So bear with me for a bit more thought about the human condition before we get to the practical aspects which deal with using subtle energies.

THE HUMAN CONSTITUTION

There is a well-known saying 'as above; so below', which comes from the ancient Greek myth of Hermes. It means that the universe or the cosmos is mirrored in humanity, the microcosm. This is a good way of explaining that as sons and daughters of mother Earth we are affected by the various frequencies or vibrations of our planet. As individuals, we also have our own frequencies which can be enhanced or denuded by those of the earth, depending on both the natural and humanised environment in which we work and live.

There has been a shift in consciousness in relation to how we view the human being. We no longer see ourselves as a collection of atoms and molecules grouped together to form organs and tissues with, hopefully, something like a soul floating above us. Modern science, through its demonstration of a universe where everything is connected, suggests the possibility that we are a system of interacting energy fields with various levels of energy extending beyond our physical body.[4]

We can then view our different levels of consciousness as belonging to a number of energy fields which connect with and interpenetrate each other. Compare this scenario with how solids, liquids and gases all interpenetrate in a handful of wet sand where we have sand, water and air. Each has its separate character and yet interacts with the other substances. Thus we are aware of sensations, feelings and thoughts as being distinct experiences which overlap. For example, touching a hot object gives us pain (physical body) which may lead to a feeling of fear (emotional body) to which our mind (mental body) responds by thinking of taking more care in the future.

While it may be stretching the newer findings of physics to fit this fairly simplistic view of psychology, the new view of the universe does see all things as connected. This gives us the freedom to make an energy-based model for planetary and human evolution.

The physics of the previous century is often called Newtonian physics after Isaac Newton. The view of scientists who followed Newton was that the universe was like a giant machine with fixed laws and rules which governed all the processes on the planet. Until the last few decades this viewpoint has been reflected by scientists in medicine and psychology in their assessment of the human being.

The view of the body as a machine gave rise to the great emphasis of specialisation in various parts of medicine and psychology. For instance in psychology, before the recent development of trans-personal psychology, the term psyche had nothing to do with the soul which was the original meaning of the term. The development of natural medicine recognises the importance of holism, which means treating the whole person. By whole person, we mean not just the whole body, but the the psyche as well which embraces both psychological functioning and spiritual direction. The natural medicine trend has been helped or underscored by the developments in physics which date from the beginning of this century.

Twentieth-century physicists discovered that the minute particles which are the basis of all forms of life are existing as both waves and particles. This dual manifestation gave rise to the particle/wave dichotomy in modern physics with a new emphasis on energy and energy fields both in the macrocosm and microcosm. The quantum paradox was born through the researches of two scientists early this century, Planck and Einstein. The basic finding of modern science is that light and other forms of energy have a dual personality – at times behaving as particles and at other times as waves.[5]

So instead of reducing the universe to ultimate particles which can be moved around to form different arrangements like parts of a machine, it became possible to focus just as legitimately on energy and energy fields. The evolving model of the interaction between universe and human beings allows for a new viewpoint on the complexity which is human life. The different levels of consciousness which we experience in our adventure of relating spirit with matter can now be envisaged as layers of energy with varying degrees of subtlety, corresponding to the many energy fields of planet Earth. Modern science has only started to explore the most obvious of these subtle energy fields.

The energy fields in the human being include the physical brain consciousness, the etheric field underlying the physical, our astral or feeling consciousness, our mental consciousness, and more subtle states which could be loosely called the soul and spiritual consciousness. I have explored these states more fully in my previous book, *Meditation, The Most Natural Therapy*.[6] In our daily living these states overlap although, as individuals, we often choose to focus on one or more levels in preference to others. These levels of energy and consciousness can all interpenetrate each other.

Each part of our being or energy level will have its own resonance or vibratory frequency and each part exists within the many vibratory possibilities on planet Earth. In this sense, there is no definite line of demarcation between our energy fields and those of another person or between ourselves and the earth. There will also be a constant interaction between all lives on our planet and between the various kingdoms in nature. From a macrocosmic perspective this is the basis for astrology and this will be further considered in chapter 3.[7]

Consider the implications of this concept of interacting energy fields. First, in a family situation each member of the family will have a profound psychological and / or physical effect on the family health, both individually and collectively. Psychologists work with this scenario every day as they seek to free their clients from the conditioning effects of family life. Although this conditioning is understood by modern society, the close interaction of energy fields is not generally considered to be the cause of such conditioning. Yet we all have the experience of wanting to get away and walk or sit by ourselves after a busy time at work, or following confinement in a small space with a group of people.

The energy field of planet Earth can be experienced by anyone walking in a forest or parkland – we say that our energies have been recharged. We do not always attribute this healing and stabilising experience to the natural health-giving resonance which can flow into our energy field from the natural magnetic field of mother Earth. We are more likely to think, 'I'm exhausted after all that talking and arguing and I just need to get away from everyone for a while.'

In the many exercises described in this book, we are dealing in particular with that level of energy we sense when we walk in the forest or by the sea. This energy comes from the etheric body of the earth and is linked to our own etheric body – the first subtle layer beyond the physical body. It is the basic energy which we acknowledge when we say that we are either weak or vital – the Qi of Chinese medicine, the Bioplasma of the Russians, the Orgone energy of Wilhelm Reich and so on. We will explore this energy in terms of the human body more fully in the next chapter.

This relationship between the etheric body of the earth and our own energy field or body, and the free flow of energy between the two is how I understand the science of earth energies which was pioneered by Fran Nixon. She had this to say in terms of our energy relationship with planet Earth:

> The world behaves as one large magnet and we as individuals are an integral part of the magnetic whole. Not only do we have a wave link characteristic of a given magnetic point, but in addition we are able to receive and link circuits with other waves in the same band of wave links which are also magnetically linked with the world's magnetism. This gives us a gigantic communication system, linking all life that is part of the same magnetic whole.[8]

THE VIVAXIS CONCEPT

Fran Nixon found that an energy relationship between our etheric energy field and that of our globe is established at some time in the last few weeks, days or hours before our birth. As I mentioned in the introduction, Vivaxis means axis of life, or the central line about which a rotating body turns. In terms of the human being, our etheric energy revolves around a central point or sphere of energies which remains in the same place throughout our life.

Some characteristics of the Vivaxis forces are similar to magnetism and indeed magnets are found to have a permanent Vivaxis or bundle of energy at the site of their creation to which they remain connected by flows of energy. Fran considered that both magnetic and gravitational forces are among the primary forces in the Vivaxis. She considered that a vertical component of magnetism is responsible for our relation to the geographical point of our Vivaxis and the horizontal wave from of the Vivaxis involves the same gravitational forces which move the tides. She further considered that the daily and monthly tides involve forces which are related to magnetic north and south. Her use of the terms gravitational and magnetic do not always correspond with the usual scientific understanding.

Much of this book is concerned with exploring the Vivaxis energies which appear to be those etheric forces which connect us with the earth in a two-way circuit which flows up one side of the body from the Vivaxis, and back down the other towards the Vivaxis (see Diagram 1). No matter how far we travel from our Vivaxis, we remain connected and can be recharged via its connection to the earth. However, there are many forces both electromagnetic, chemical and psychic which can interfere with our Vivaxis channel and it is important to be able to diagnose and clear ourselves of these disturbances. In chapter 5 we will take up the subject of the Vivaxis in further detail with exercises for finding its direction and use.

In the meantime, with the above thoughts in mind, we start in

Diagram 1

DIRECTION OF TWO-WAY FLOW FACING OUR VIVAXIS

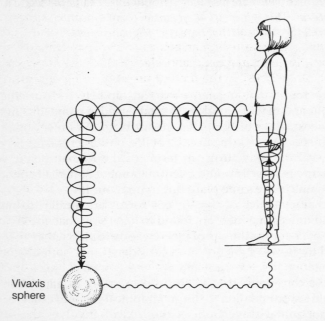

Vivaxis
sphere

Vivaxis forces remain whether we are near or far from our birth location.

this chapter to explore our life energy as it relates to mother Earth and to explore some techniques which will help us to absorb the life-giving energies of our planet.

As a natural therapist I have used therapies for decades to give people more energy. However, in conjunction with our psychological state, our basic physical lifestyle and environment must always be understood as the backdrop for any therapeutic aid. If we compromise the integrity of our body energies, the effect of vitamins, minerals, herbs, homeopathy, or Vivaxis energies is greatly diminished – like pouring water into a bottomless pit. Some of the ways we diminish our health include poor diet, a noisy and polluted environment, introducing conflicting energies from man-made electrical sources, and negative thoughts and emotions. So our first task on the road to better health is to free the body from those disturbances which cause a conflict of energies.

OUR FACULTIES FOR FINDING PLANETARY DIRECTIONS

We have looked briefly at the subtle parts of our constitution and at the concept of human beings, and Earth, having interconnecting and interpenetrating energy fields. We have highlighted the role of energy in both the macrocosm (planet) and microcosm (man). I believe that in the future human beings will learn much more about themselves in both magnetic and electrical terms. However, we must not be restricted to the present understanding and measurements of physics. There are electrical polarities and magnetic affinities and fields at the etheric and more subtle levels and our physical instruments can only take measurements indirectly. In this book you will learn to use your body as an instrument for sensing and testing these energies.

As suggested, we already experience ourselves as being composed of many subtle interacting fields and vehicles. Therefore we can use our own etheric body as an instrument for evaluating etheric energies. We can devise and repeat experiments where we can check our findings with others and thus bring repeatability and cross-referencing into our research. We can even devise experiments where neither the tester nor operator knows the nature of the materials being used – the famous double blind trials of medical science. In other words, we can work in a scientific manner using our body as an instrument.

Careful discrimination will enable you to distinguish between etheric and psychic energies; this is most important because of the interpenetration of these fields. Many people working with subtle energies lose their credibility because they confuse the etheric body or the more subtle part of the physical body with the astral body and psychic energies. Their findings then become confused and conditioned by their desires and wishes and reliable information is not conveyed. We then move into the area of the fortune-teller and realm of glamour.

We will now look at the interface between the etheric and physical levels of energy. This lies in the electromagnetic sphere and can be measured on both the planet and humans by the instruments of physics. Our consideration of this topic will give us some clues to our own inherent magnetic sense. We will learn to use this subtle sense in order to become more familiar with our energy body.

We are bathed in the electromagnetic field of the earth and at any point on the surface we move in a sea of energy that exists between the surface of the earth and the ionosphere which has been found to have an electrical potential of 400 volts per square metre. This means that there is a difference in electrical potential between the surface of the earth which is charged negatively, and the lower surface of the ionosphere which is 80 kilometres above the earth and which is charged positively.[9] We feel so comfortable in this field which vibrates about 7.5 cycles per second (the Schumann waves) that the early astronauts suffered until these waves were generated in their space capsules.

Medical researcher Robert Becker considers that electromagnetic energy has now been returned to a position of prominence in understanding both human and geophysical phenomena. Becker points out that with the sophistication of modern instruments it has been revealed that living creatures are intimately related to the earth's geomagnetic field and derive vital basic information from it.[10] No statement could better underscore the basis for this book.

Scientists have found that many living creatures with a sense of direction including bees, pigeons and fish have a substance called magnetite embedded in their heads. Research by the geosciences department at the University of California found that whales and dolphins also have similar faculties for their survival and that whale stranding occurs at points of low field strength. It appears that whales travel along magnetic troughs which run from north to south. Even small creatures like salamanders have been found to have separate magnetic navigational systems.

According to Becker, *'the magnetite-containing magnetic organ that is probably present in most life forms including humans is closely connected to the brain. It has been shown unequivocally to be a sense organ that informs the organism of the direction of the earth's magnetic field'.* Becker goes on to say *'it is possible that it (the magnetic organ) is also sensitive to and reports information on the micropulsation frequencies although this aspect has not been studied'.*[11]

In the light of Fran Nixon's discoveries, Becker's statements are most interesting for we shall be shortly describing how to find magnetic north by visualising the frequency of sodium which relates to the magnetic north pole. Dr Robin Baker at the University of Manchester in England has added to our understanding of the magnetic sense by locating a magnetic focus of activity at the back of the nasal passage and just in front of the pituitary gland – the ethnoid sinus. He found that humans can sense magnetic north and this sensing is disturbed for up to two hours after having a bar magnet placed across their forehead for fifteen minutes.[12]

In other words, the bar magnet disturbs the normal orientation of our magnetite crystals and this confirms Fran Nixon's experiments on disturbances caused by application of magnets to the body. The pineal gland has also been found to be sensitive to the changing pattern of the earth's magnetic field and may well be involved.

In summary, we can say that our sensing of external fields is mediated through two highly sophisticated internal organs which are both connected to the nervous system – the magnetic organ containing minute crystals of magnetite and the endocrine gland called the pineal which passes its secretions directly into the blood. These structures help us learn the skills described in this book but first we must remove factors which interfere with their functioning such as effects from X-rays, magnets and electromagnetic fields.

REMOVAL OF ENERGY DISTURBANCES – THE EFFECT OF X-RAYS

A common problem with our own electromagnetic field and hence our energy body is the effect of old X-rays. Most of us have had X-rays of some kind whether for broken limbs, chiropractic treatment or dentistry. Fran Nixon found that after an X-ray, the carbon atoms in our bones take on a disturbed direction which does not disappear with the passage of time. Normally, the carbon and calcium atoms of our bones have wave or energy directions towards both our Vivaxis and to true north and south on our planet[13] (see Diagram 2).

Over the years, Fran found that when there is a disturbance to the carbon atoms especially in the back area, backaches, disc trouble and muscle problems are prevalent. Once you have developed the technique of recording your body energies you can test the profound effect of X-rays on the body. This does not mean that we should never allow ourselves to be X-rayed, but we should understand the implications and take measures to restore the body integrity.

A very simple technique has been developed to remove the effect of X-rays. It consists of applying carbon frequencies to all parts of the body. Carbon appears to have an important role in maintaining correct energy flows through the bones. Applications of carbon to the body are therefore valuable after exposure to ionising radiation such as occurs in X-rays.

In this book when we refer to elements and their effect on the body, we are referring to the energy or frequencies of the substance and not to actual physical molecules. Thus when we apply carbon to the body, we produce changes in the frequency of our carbon atoms. You don't need to eat or inject carbon in the usual physical sense. The same principle applies in the science of homeopathy which is briefly discussed in the next chapter.

Diagram 2

**EFFECTS OF X-RAYS ON THE ENERGIES
IN OUR BONES**

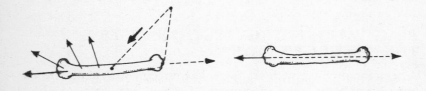

Bone not aligned to
its Vivaxis indicating
confusion of energies.

Bone aligned to its
Vivaxis showing a
coherent flow of energies.

CLEARING TECHNIQUES WITH CARBON

1 Collect some charcoal (carbon) from a fire made with untreated wood and place it in a strong plastic bag. The amount of charcoal should be enough so that the bag will cover about 15 sq cm of your body.

2 Stand facing approximately north and place the plastic bag containing charcoal on your head while focussing your thoughts on carbon for about thirty seconds. Then continue by applying the charcoal to your arms, chest (front and back), lower body and legs. Each area should be jarred with the heel of your hand to stir up the disturbed energies before applying the charcoal. Wrists, elbows, shoulders, coccyx, knees and jaw may need special attention.

3 It is best to treat your body in sections. After applying the charcoal to your head and arms, this carbon energy should be balanced by moving the bag of charcoal away, facing south and thinking of calcium. Fran found calcium to be a pair with carbon and their compass directions are always directly in opposition. Continue to treat the rest of the body in this manner.

4 Pay special attention to any previously X-rayed areas. To remove the effect of dental X-rays, wrap a small piece of charcoal in plastic, then press and 'chomp' it between your teeth and on to the roof of your mouth.

5 Carbon should be applied to both plantar (sole) and dorsal surfaces of your foot. Stamp each foot after activation by the carbon.

Remember that the affected area is always larger than the X-rayed area due to the scattering effect of X-rays. Hips, pelvic bones and knee joints can be stimulated by a good Hawaiian Hula motion while holding the carbon on the bones concerned. If you have difficulty reaching your back, a stocking filled with dried beans makes a convenient tool for stimulating your spine before applying the charcoal.

Once you have learnt to find the earth's energy layers or bands, this clearing procedure is enhanced while facing west on Force Flow 1 – the carbon flow. As the carbon energy is related to this flow, the effect of absorbing carbon will be enhanced. Until you have learnt how to find the energy layers, you should face north as previously directed.

FINDING TRUE NORTH AND SOUTH

After the clearing exercise with the carbon, you should be able to find the directions of true north and south through the natural magnetic response in your body to the compass directions for carbon and calcium. For some reason these elements are associated with true north and south. (Later, you will learn to find the wave pattern and the direction for all the life-giving elements.)

1 Stand on level ground and place your hands firmly on your thighs with your feet together.

2 Visualise the element carbon. In doing this your energy body will become attuned to the frequency of carbon which 'travels' over the planet in the direction of true north. You should feel a strong pull in your body towards true north.

Diagram 3

CARBON AND CALCIUM PULLS

By facing north and visualising carbon you experience a forward pull through the influence of the North Pole force flow on your carbon atoms. Hands must be flat on thighs.

By facing north and visualising calcium you experience a backward pull through the influence of the South Pole force flow on our calcium atoms.

3 Visualise calcium (white blackboard chalk) and you will get a pull towards true south (see Diagram 3).

The only extra information needed for finding these directions is contained in chapter 2 and concerns the fact that the frequencies of calcium and carbon are interrupted several times each twenty-four hours, due to the changing relationship between sun, moon, and earth which causes the daily tides. Until you know how to find the tides, you will not know when the horizontal directions or vectors for calcium and carbon disappear. However, during those periods when the horizontal waves have disappeared, you can find the carbon and calcium pulls using their vertical waves. Place your hands against your thighs as before but close your hand so that your fingers are pointing upwards, and are thus able to respond to the vertical waves of carbon and calcium.

So, if you find no response in your body by holding your hands flat on your thighs when visualising carbon, try holding your hands as a closed fist on your thighs. You may wonder why we don't wait to do this exercise in chapter 2 when we have more information about the tides. From much practice with students I have found it best to start an exercise that deals with the element used in the clearing exercise. Also, the carbon and calcium pulls confirm that the clearing exercise has been satisfactorily completed.

While true north and south are related to carbon and calcium, magnetic north and south are related to the frequencies of sea salt and iron respectively. To find magnetic north, we visualise sea salt, and for magnetic south, we visualise iron. Again, the body should be pulled towards the source of the element which is visualised. Magnetic north is a variable degree east of true north. Indeed, the magnetic poles have moved many times during our planetary history. This has been found by scientists who investigate the right and left-hand spin of molecules preserved in the crust of the earth.

Finding north and south can be very handy if you're bush-walking on a dull day when it is hard to tell the sun's position. If you are unable to do this exercise correctly, repeat it after doing the neutralising exercise which follows, as you may still have a confusion of energies from foreign fields.

An interesting piece of information about the elements carbon and oxygen was mentioned by Lovelock in his book about Gaia. He said that several scientists had attributed the amount of oxygen in the atmosphere to carbon burial and its release by the weathering of siliceous rocks, and to the processes of methane production. This contrasts with the more widely-accepted hypothesis of oxygen production and release from living plants and trees. One could argue of course that if there were no forests there would eventually be no carbon so that vegetation is still the indirect cause of oxygen production.

In the context of the Lovelock hypothesis, I think it relevant that Fran Nixon discovered that the frequencies of carbon and oxygen are connected and that for health we need a good alignment to these frequencies which we find both relate to north. She also discovered that carbon, calcium and oxygen are related to key flows of energy on the surface of the planet and these flows relate to our own individual energy or Vivaxis flows (see chapter 4).

This relationship between carbon and its pair calcium, and between oxygen and its pair cobalt derives from the fact that they are directly opposite each other in terms of the compass. Their directions in space are the first of many patterns which will emerge in this book. You will learn to check these patterns with your body. Further research into these frequencies will no doubt eventually give more understanding as to why the elements relate to different directions of the compass.

Canadian researchers of Vivaxis discovered that a field of energy can be created between a plastic bag of carbon and some white blackboard chalk (calcium) placed 25 cm (10 inches) apart. This field is able to cancel the detrimental field created by magnets. Their research project involved placing four bar magnets, each of 1200 gauss strength, in the four directions of the compass. Gauss is the unit of measurement for magnetic fields. A strong vertical vector of energy was found at the centre point between the magnets. The carbon was placed north-east between two of the magnets and the calcium between the other two magnets at south-west. The vertical field from the magnets was now found to be cancelled.

This finding certainly proves the benefit of using the frequencies of calcium and carbon to counteract detrimental fields. Magnets on the human body or used near the human body can introduce a foreign field of energies into our own circuits. Many people have disturbed their energy circuits through regular applications of magnets for pain even while receiving temporary relief.

FOREIGN ENERGY FIELDS

Apart from magnetic interference and X-ray treatments there are a number of other reasons why individuals can manifest a great confusion of energies in their energy field. Possible causes of foreign fields are reflexology, cardiograms, diapulse and diathermy machines, and at times, even contact healing. A foreign energy field establishes a permanent link with frequencies which are not compatible with our own frequencies. So while we still have a connection to our own Vivaxis we are also connected to a foreign Vivaxis. This causes a chaotic condition of energies in our etheric body.

The creation of a foreign Vivaxis happens as follows. When we connect to a machine with an electromagnetic field such as a diathermy machine or a therapy unit with a pulsed electromagnetic wave, our own frequencies are combined with those of the Vivaxis related to that machine. Earlier it was explained that a Vivaxis is created when a magnet is made. Any machine using electromagnetic energy will be found to have an associated Vivaxis phenomena.

Alternatively, we might be connected to the Vivaxis of a therapist. This may happen when the therapist holds bi-lateral points on our meridians as occurs in shiatsu or applied kinesiology. In this case, the normal routes to both Vivaxes are temporarily blocked and the wavelengths or frequencies are combined so that the circuit is completed. This forms a new Vivaxis at the site of the treatment which permanantly remains at that site.

Now the client may well have initial improvement to the treated area in question because the energy flow of the new Vivaxis blocks the pain impulse to the brain. However, the ultimate result is that the client's brain and receptors become connected to two Vivaxes. This causes congestion and chaos in our energy fields because there are now two sets of frequencies being received by our system at all times.

Symptoms of a foreign field will possibly include headaches, poor memory, confusion, muscle pains, and exhaustion – indeed many symptoms which are now grouped under the heading of chronic fatigue syndrome. This may be the reason why these patients are so therapy resistant and why common natural therapies do not always help. The disturbance in brain receptors may also be the basic cause of the large increase in Alzheimer's disease.

If we have a foreign field, these energies are always impinging on our own frequencies and energies even when we are physically and mentally resting. It is wise to presume that we may have some foreign fields and the following technique will help in their removal.

Techniques to Remove Foreign Energy Fields

The rationale for this process is to bring in and saturate our energy field with its own energies so strongly that any foreign-induced energies are removed. To accentuate our own energies we make circuits with the fingertips and toes touching in the following manner.

NEUTRALISING EXERCISE – LONG VERSION

1 Find a quiet place where you will not be disturbed and assume a sitting position (see Diagram 4). Place the centre whorls of your fingers together and likewise your toes. Your heels should also be touching.

2 Firmly press the fingertips and palms of your hands together while inhaling.

3 During exhalation release the pressure on your fingertips but keep them touching. Your hands should move as if you are playing an accordion. Provided your fingertips and toes stay connected, you can take short rests during this exercise.

4 Keep the exercise going for a full five minutes.

5 Keep your toes and heels in close contact throughout. At intervals briefly press and release pressure on your toes and heels.

6 It is very important to hold your arms away from your body so that the energies are not short-circuited on your clothing.

You need to exert considerable pressure on the hands in order for this exercise to be effective. However, pressure should be applied in such a manner that it will stimulate energy flow and not restrict circulation. It is useful for therapists to undertake a short version of this exercise in-between each patient consultation as it prevents the energies of the therapist being drained by the client and, more importantly, prevents the formation of a foreign Vivaxis between client and therapist.

NEUTRALISING EXERCISE – SHORT VERSION

1 Stand with knees and ankles pressed together.

2 Make a circuit between your fingertips and use the same press and release technique while inhaling and exhaling for one minute.

Diagram 4

CLOSED CIRCUIT NEUTRALISING EXERCISES

Long version

• Exhale and release pressure—arms must be kept from touching other parts of the body. An accordion motion is used. Continue for five minutes.
• Inhale and press hands together.

Short version

Ankles and knees must be touching. Complete in thirty seconds.

Like the carbon clearing exercise, the neutralising exercise is enhanced when it is performed on Force Flow 1. It can be repeated later if necessary on that force flow. Both these exercises should be done between high and low tide times (solunar flow) which is explained in chapter 3. In the meantime, we cover the possibility that the exercise was undertaken during high or low tide, by repeating it the following day at least two hours earlier or later than our first practice.

The clearing exercises and direction finding underpin all the techniques described in this book. Without cleared circuits we are unable to test energies accurately. Finding directions on our planet is a good start to the adventure in earth energies. Next, we look at the whole concept of those vibrations and frequencies that we can test and feel.

2
PLANETARY VIBRATIONS AND FREQUENCIES

★ ★ ★ ★ ★ ★

W E HAVE looked briefly at the big picture in terms of spirit, energy and matter and their interaction on our planet and also their relation to our human constitution. Now we'll examine energy, vibration and frequency in more detail to help us understand the practical exercises throughout this book involving our energies as they relate to planet Earth.

THE MEANING OF VIBRATION AND FREQUENCY

Energy generally manifests in waves. Frequency means the number of waves manifesting per second counted from the peak of one to the next. The electromagnetic spectrum in our universe is made up of waves of a wide range of frequency and amplitude (height of the wave). The frequency ranges from the extra low frequencies (ELF) as for example from power lines, to X-rays and microwaves which have very high frequencies. Our bodies like even slower waves which are in the alpha range of about 8–12 cycles (hertz) per second. This is the same frequency which is found on the planet in its natural state and these background planetary waves are called Schumann waves.

An energy field consists of many waves which are vibrating at a particular frequency. For instance, you may know that there is an electromagnetic field around a wire carrying electricity. In Australia and Europe this field is vibrating at 50 hertz and in the USA and Canada the rate is 60 hertz. This means there is a wave frequency of 50 or 60 cycles per second and this is an example of a low frequency field (ELF).

If we strike the note C on the piano, the associated piano string will vibrate at 256 waves or cycles per second. We hear in a range between 16 and 25,000 hertz. Some animals can hear much higher frequencies. Frequencies in our visual range will be different again. Ultrasound, radio frequencies, X-rays and infra-red all have their own frequency range in the electromagnetic spectrum. The electromagnetic field of all our household gadgets is around 50 cycles per second. This is an important point to remember for our later discussion on the possible damage inflicted on our energy fields by these environmental and household electromagnetic fields.

Everything on our planet is vibrating at particular frequencies including our various organs and tissues. We must also consider the frequencies of our emotions and thoughts. Our inner feelings and thoughts have a conditioning effect on our psychic energy which in turn is constantly sending out subtle vibrations into the environment thus affecting other humans, animals and plants around us.

The range of frequencies of these psychic vibrations is obviously much more subtle than the normal electromagnetic spectrum. Psychic fields cannot be measured with physical instruments, however, the effect of changing moods on our electromagnetic field has been observed through high frequency photography. This type of photography is undertaken by placing a person in a high frequency field which shows their electromagnetic field on a photographic plate. It is called Kirlian photography after the person who first noticed the effect, in Russia in 1938.

The aura of a person in an aroused emotional state such as anger often features the colour red in this type of photography. Research has established that it is the type of salt in a person's sweat which provides a particular colour in the photograph. The skin gives off electrons in the presence of the high frequency field and these collide with molecules in the air to form the lighted corona or aura around the subject in the photo.

When we start to think in terms of frequency or of vibrating or oscillating fields, consider as a hypothetical example, the effect of a person with an energy field vibrating at 90,000 hertz on the field of an individual who may on this particular occasion be vibrating at between 10–30,000 hertz? Of course, this is an oversimplification. Our emotional field will be vibrating at a number of different rates as are all the different organs in our body. But there will be an overall effect which will vary according to whether we are feeling depression, anger, sadness or joy and creativity.

The following practical example is a good physical analogy which explains how we affect our environment. Imagine a room in which we place five grandfather clocks with their pendulums all swinging out of sequence. It has been found that, after a certain period of time, the process of entrainment takes place whereby all the pendulums will eventually swing together in simultaneous rhythm.

Translate this to the human kingdom and we have a good explanation for mob psychology. So, if we are in a group whose basic frequency does not match our own, it is possible our energy field may be overwhelmed by the predominant frequency. This may be experienced as either pleasant or unpleasant according to the prevailing frequency. In the company of a person suffering from depression it is quite difficult not to take on their negative mood to some extent. The struggle to maintain our own rhythm may be exhausting. Conversely, a joyful person may lift our spirits. Teachers are well aware of the effect on the class of one disruptive child who may in turn be reflecting turmoil and aggression from home. The various frequencies of thoughts and emotions have yet to be precisely tabulated.

HOW DO WE MEASURE VIBRATION OR FREQUENCY?

Instruments such as the spectro-photometer give an indication of elements according to their relative frequency in the electro-magnetic range. More importantly, we can use our bodies for measuring subtle energies. In chapter 1, we established how to find magnetic and other planetary directions using the body as an instrument for testing energies. In this chapter we will explore how to use the body as an instrument to check energy flows and vibratory frequencies in both our own body and the environment. We are basically using the same sense that is employed by people who practise dowsing, or water divining.

Many individual practitioners of natural therapies and various schools of thought have established guidelines for the correct vibratory frequencies for every organ and tissue in the body. Some have gone further and established frequencies for the energy centres in our subtle bodies – the chakras. Perhaps the first group to establish particular rates were the radionic practitioners. David Tansley was a well-respected radionic practitioner who placed this form of diagnosis and treatment into a broad framework which included both science and the ancient wisdom.[1]

The practice of dowsing involves using the extra-sensory faculty of touch to feel vibrations. The scientific rationale of dowsing refers to the tiny magnetic crystals embedded in the brain (see page 10) and a possible connection with the pineal gland. In addition, a French scientist, Professor Yves Rocard, was reported in the journal *Nature* as having found other magnetically sensitive points on the body including the brow ridges and some articulations of the vertebrae. He saw these as crucial receptors in the dowsing process.[2]

I would suggest that using the body to sense energies includes both our magnetic sense which is associated with the magnetite crystals, plus the use of our etheric centres (see chapter 8). These centres in turn are mediated by the pineal gland to influence our electromagnetic field, and from there to the nervous system. Many of the substances which we are exploring in the exercises in this book are not magnetic in the usual sense of the word and therefore, as suggested by Becker, may be sensed with a faculty of the pineal gland.

Most people use some apparatus to help them develop and amplify the dowsing sense. The simplest aid can be a pendulum or two metal rods which are usually bent to form a right angle. There are various kinds of dowsing rods made of both inorganic and metallic materials and more sophisticated models which enhance the fine movements of our body to make the perceived vibration more obvious.

The dowser must hold the rods out in front, keeping the horizontal arm of the rod quite parallel to the ground. They need to establish what each movement of the rod means and this will vary from person to person. The rods may swing in one direction for a 'yes' response and in another for a 'no' response. The dowser then proceeds to ask questions about the subject and to visualise the subject under consideration. The minute reactions in their nervous system in response to the questions are amplified by the pendulum or rods.

It is hard to imagine how this process works with map dowsing but perhaps the more subtle psychic faculties work in this case.

Some practitioners use the pendulum to ask questions of a more psychological nature. Once psychic energy is involved the accuracy of the response is in doubt. The practitioner must have very stable emotions and an unbiased mind or the answer will be conditioned by their own psyche.

Radionic practitioners developed quite elaborate instruments with dials and wires. In the early days these machines often had a rubber diaphragm and practitioners would move their fingers across it adjusting the dials to different frequencies as they diagnosed a person or specimen. When they struck the rate which corresponded with the vibration of the tissue or organ concerned they would get a 'stick' which meant their fingers would not move so easily over the powdered surface of the rubber. Amusing incidents are described in the literature where some practitioners obtained the same results irrespective of whether the machine was plugged into the power source, and this indicates that the process is basically related to the subjective ability of the practitioner.

The various normal rates for healthy organs were established by trial and error over many years. A remedy such as a homeopathic medicine or flower essence would be matched to the disease rate to restore the part concerned to the normal rate. Refinements to these radionic instruments have been developed over the years although in each case it is the subjective or subtle response of the practitioner which establishes the diagnosis. Since 1950, a number of electronic instruments for diagnosis have come on to the market. One of the most popular in Europe, USA and Australia is the Vegatest and it is discussed in an earlier book of mine, *Frontiers of Natural Therapies*.[3]

The Vega instrument is partially a radionic device. It measures skin resistance as the practitioner places various ampoules into the circuitry to establish a number of factors including chronicity of disease, the most disturbed organs, and the appropriate remedies. The instrument can be used in an open-ended manner for any number of inquiries. However, the assessment is in part dependent on the faculties of the practitioner and the response of the needle appears to be conditioned through a psycho-kinesic effect from the practitioner. This means the psychic energy from the practitioner is involved in the response of the instrument.

More recent diagnostic tools are claimed by their manufacturers to measure the frequencies of the patient via skin resistance without subjective input from the therapist. It is possible that they are translating etheric energies into electromagnetic frequencies but we must be alert to the fact that any assessment of another person even via an electronic device may be conditioned by our emotions and thoughts. Even twentieth-century physics has demonstrated that in scientific experiments, the results will tend to be influenced to some extent by the researcher.

A clear example of the influence of human beings on empirical data is the anomaly in modern physics that the mass of a particle cannot be measured at the same time as its position or momentum. It is said that as soon as we focus on the particle its wave function collapses. It is almost as if the moment that we have the intention to measure or focus on the object it changes. So we are either measuring it as a wave of energy or as a particle with mass and position.[4] For this reason it is preferable for people to test their own energies using their own etheric body as the instrument.

When we use our bodies to measure subtle energies it is essential that we have serene emotions and a quiet and open mind to achieve accuracy. We need to be able to work in a detached manner and literally to use the mind as the 'common sense'. This enables us to overcome the usual situation where the mind is constantly conditioned by past events and by our emotional states. True commonsense can thus develop and the mind can make a valuable synthesis of information received through the senses of sight, hearing, touch, etc. and in this way is used as a sense organ. Regular meditation is a great asset to this process.

The scientist De Broglie first established in 1925 that everything does have its own specific frequency or vibration.[5] In fact an instrument called an oscilloscope gives a visual representation of the electrical frequency of elements. This is a consistent procedure and quite a different approach from the subjective procedure used by radionics practitioners to establish frequencies using the dowsing sense. In time, perhaps, a correlation may be found between the two approaches.

ORTHODOX MEDICINE AND NATURAL THERAPIES

As we have discussed, there are two basic streams of medicine which can work together in a complementary way. Orthodox medicine has been largely based on Newtonian physics and sees the body as a machine. When a part wears out it is often fixed or replaced. Specialists dealing with one set of parts do not necessarily have a great understanding or interest in other parts.

This approach pays scant attention to holism. The feelings and thoughts of the person are rarely taken into account in the treatment prescribed unless they become obstructive to the medical procedure. In cases of severe infection, antibiotics or steroids are administered to resolve the crisis. The underlying energies of the body are not acknowledged or addressed except as existing at the cellular level in biochemical activity. Of course I am generalising and we all know of dedicated medical people who are very sensitive to the larger situation of their patients.

Natural therapy is concerned in particular to enhance and balance the energies or vibrational frequencies of the body. It includes vitamins, minerals, herbs, homeopathy, flower essences, colour, sound, acupuncture, body work based on the Chinese meridian system, and earth energies. The significant factor in each therapy is the effect on our body energies or energy field. Holism is inherent in the philosophy of natural medicine because each part of the body is understood to be intimately connected with all other parts through the energy fields. In each therapy, the natural remedies restore the healthy rhythm, vibration and harmony to the area which has lost its ease and which has therefore become dis-eased.

Natural medicine is preventive medicine because it strengthens our natural immunity by enhancing and balancing our basic energies. Skilled natural therapists can observe detrimental changes in body energies before clinical pathology manifests. This was proven by Harold Saxton Burr as early as 1938 with his experiments on the human energy or Life field (L-field) as he called it. Burr was involved with an experiment whereby the L-fields of 1000 women were checked. Of the 102 women who showed disturbed energies, 96 were later found to have abnormal or malignant cells.[6]

Orthodox medicine and natural therapies are not mutually exclusive. There will always be people who will not work with nature and who push their body to the stage where emergency measures are needed if life is to be preserved, sometimes at cost of a limb or organ. Natural therapies can help even in these situations to prepare the body for surgery and to aid in recuperation from surgery or serious infection. Other medical situations such as cardiac conditions and severe infections benefit from a combination of both approaches. There is opportunity for teamwork and already I know of a number of health centres where natural therapists have referrals from orthodox medical doctors.

NATURAL THERAPIES IN RELATION TO MOTHER EARTH

Most natural therapies come from the earth. It is true though that technology is now used to prepare herbs, flower essences, vitamins and homeopathic remedies. Generally manufacturers of these products use technology which does not destroy the life force of the remedy. Unlike pharmaceutical manufacturers, natural preparations contain all the balanced ingredients of a herb and this approach prevents side-effects.

Traditional Chinese medicine is intimately related to the seasons and cycles of planet earth. It has five elements which occur in a continuous cycle – spring (wood) gives rise to summer (fire) followed by late summer (earth) and then fall or autumn (metal or air) moves to winter (water). Each element relates to a main organ system – wood to liver and gall bladder, fire to heart and small intestine, earth to spleen and stomach, metal or air to lungs and colon, and water to kidney and bladder.

In every system of natural medicine, practitioners must deal with energy blocks which cause toxins to accumulate. Removing these blocks improves and balances energies. The more esoteric schools of thought understand that for disease to occur there will be an inner and an outer factor. The inner factor will be disturbed thoughts and emotions which may have ancient origins going back even to previous lives, or if one prefers the psychological approach of Jung, to the racial unconscious. The philosophy of esotericists such as Alice Bailey describes disease as the outcome of both factors rather than one leading to the other.[7]

It seems only a matter of time until a system is devised to establish the vibratory rates of all natural therapies which will then be matched to the diagnosed frequency of the disturbed part. This has already been established to some extent in homeopathy where each remedy is carefully matched to the diseased state of the individual client. The disadvantage is that it takes many years for a person to accumulate sufficient knowledge to be a successful homeopath and, because of the detail involved in assessing each case, diagnosis can take a long time.

Computer programmes have alleviated much tedious work in homeopathic case taking and may be useful in selecting the remedy. The problem of establishing the appropriate potency of the remedy remains. The medicine must be measured against the exact vibratory frequency of each person and and their disease and the exact potency and dose of the medicine selected.

One person may require a dose of the homeopathic remedy diluted to 3,000 parts in the solution while another person will require a dilution of 3,000,000 parts. The system of dilution used by homeopathic chemists is usually based on the decimal or centesimal system. In the case of the centesimal system, one drop would be mixed with one hundred drops of water and shaken. A further drop of the subsequent mixture would be added and mixed with another hundred drops of water and this process repeated for as many times as necessary. After the twenty-fifth dilution there will be no physical molecules left. This was established mathematically by Avogadro and hence science talks about Avogadro's number as a particular dilution of a chemical substance where no physical molecule of the substance remains.

Consider the case of two people needing the snake poison Lachesis; both of them may have the same symptoms but their energy fields which condition physical health will oscillate or vibrate at quite different frequencies. Over many years the skilled homeopath learns to discern the sensitivity and susceptibility of individuals to a remedy.

The dilution of homeopathic remedies appears to provide the harmonics or overtones to the original remedy in the same way that a note on a musical instrument will have overtones. Having chosen the correct remedy, it will shatter the disease process in the same way that a singer can shatter a glass if they sing the exact note corresponding to the resonance of the glass. This is called the healing crisis and it can be be accompanied by a shift and re-balancing of energy which may manifest as fever and elimination of toxic matter from the normal channels of the body such as skin, bowels, kidneys and lungs. This process may take some weeks following the administration of the remedy.

It appears that the application and use of sound as therapy may also be a very specific way of applying the necessary vibration. This very subtle approach to vibrational therapy brings us closer to the main theme of the book; that is using healing energies from the earth which have no physical form unlike minerals, herbs and most natural supplements.

THE APPLICATION OF SOUND AS HEALING FREQUENCIES

In 1992, I visited the clinic of Dr Peter Guy Manners who practises in Bretforten, a beautiful little village in the Cotswold country of the

United Kingdom. Manners has developed a system of therapy called Cymatics which is based on the work of Hans Jenny, a Swiss scientist who studied the effect of sound waves and different frequencies on inorganic matter. Cymatics comes from the Greek work kyma which means wave. Hans Jenny found that his experimental substances under the influence of different frequencies took on well-known shapes such as sea creatures, human organs and plant life.[8] It appears that sound has a very formative effect and that all forms on our planet may be precipitated by sound.

Manners set about applying this concept to healing the body. He explained that with the assistance of acoustic engineers he 'wired up' volunteer medical students to establish the vibratory frequency of all the body organs and tissues in their healthy state. These sounds were then put on tape and played through a special vibrator head which was moved over the skin of the patient. The affected body part was treated for about ten minutes to restore the correct frequency. Recently Manners computerised the system so that the tapes are no longer needed and a modern electronic treatment unit is used. The sound is still applied to the body in the same way through the vibrator.

Further evidence for the healing effect of sound has emerged. At the end of 1994, I attended a seminar conducted by Sharry Edwards entitled Signature Sound. She told us how she began hearing sounds which she could not identify and how she concluded that she must have tinnitus – an aggravating condition of the ear which causes hissing or other irritating sounds. On examination, an audiologist found she had a range of hearing beyond any he had encountered. She actually hears sounds which are transmitted by our ears and her later research demonstrated that each person transmits the frequency from their ear which is needed for their own healing. The transmission of the correct note by the ear is an effort by the body to heal itself

Sharry Edwards found that the note (or frequency) a particular person needs is also missing from their voice and that by receiving this vibration as treatment, their voice eventually produces the healing sound again. This finding was established decades ago by the now famous French physician Alfred Tomatis who found that the voice could only produce what the ear hears. He found that many people cut out particular sounds from their environment even before birth to avoid psychological pain caused by negative relationships with those close to them.

Tomatis found that usually the missing sounds in the voice were the high frequency sounds and that these can be restored. He made recordings using an electronic ear to filter out the low frequencies of music which he chose from amongst classical composers such as Mozart. The filtered music was then applied as therapy through a speaker.[9] In time the client is able to 'hear' these sounds missed by their ears without the assistance of the tapes.

Through testing and computerising sounds, Sharry Edwards has correlated particular notes or frequencies with all the organs and tissues in the body; with all the known elements in nature; and with both pharmaceutical products and natural remedies. With her co-workers, a system of diagnosis has been developed which includes electronic hardware and a software programme to chart the voice and to work out the note most relevant for healing. This frequency is then applied by a specially designed unit which is used daily for as long as needed to correct the condition.

I was interested that Sharry has worked on the psychological manifestations of the missing frequency and she found that this frequency relates in eighty per cent of cases to the astrological birth date. Other students of sound have correlated the Western musical scale to the signs of the zodiac. These people include Ptolemy, Kepler, Heindel and more recently, Joscelyn Godwin. The most popular arrangement is for the note C to be correlated with Aries, C# with Taurus, D with Gemini and so on through the musical scale and the twelve signs of the zodiac.[10]

These discoveries about sound lead us back to the ancient teachings of Pythagoras that everything in our solar system relates to the musical scale or basic frequencies which correspond to the ratios between the planets and their furthest distance from the sun. We begin to see how subtle energies from our planet like the Vivaxis energies may reflect this cosmic music and be used to heal our bodies or form nature.

We have looked at the meaning of vibration and frequency, and how natural therapies are really energy medicine. In summary, the basic principle is to restore the right vibration and frequency to our bodies and the environment, so that we are in harmony with planet Earth. There are as yet no instruments available which objectively match the correct natural therapy with the exact body frequency needed. We are coming closer with the use of various electronic instruments but the most precise instrument to use is our body. In the next section, we will learn to use the body as an exact instrument for evaluating the energies in our body and the environment.

USING OUR BODY AS AN INSTRUMENT FOR DIAGNOSIS

In 1980, Fran Nixon taught me how to check energy flows through my body and how to find energy blocks without the use of any expensive instrumentation and without even needing a pendulum. She called this approach to diagnosis – testing the ion flow.[11] As some readers will know, an ion is the term used for a charged particle. We have positive and negative ions in the atmosphere and in our body. Scientists have found that ions are continually discharged from the skin.

An ion is an atom or group of atoms possessing an electric charge. An excess of electrons gives a negative charge, and conversely, a loss of electrons gives a positive charge. In terms of our planetary life, the ion flow is associated with magnetic north and south. It has been found that in times of extreme weather conditions, or during earthquakes, the ion flow of the planetary area involving the disturbance is affected. In the Northern Hemisphere, hot winds from the south have been found to make people irritable because they bring or create an excess of positive ions. In the Southern Hemisphere, the hot north winds have the same effect.

The manifestation of an ion flow in the body is, I believe, very basic to good health as the etheric body and its associated electromagnetic field appear to be intimately related to ion flow. Fran Nixon found that the ion flow in the body can be measured by using the arm as a recording device. Your arm in recording ion flow will move back and forth, first away from and then towards your body at about the same speed as your heartbeat. You can prove this by exercising vigorously and noting that the subsequent movement of your arm on ceasing exercise is much faster than before. The exact technique will be described shortly.

In the presence of an energy block or a foreign field, no ion flow is recorded at all. Please note that we are not considering here blocks associated with heart problems but stasis of energy in any part of the body.

I have found that some people who have many energy conflicts can appear to record ion flow very easily, but on closer examination the arm is found to be moving in many directions. The lack of clear rhythm in these people is due to an excess of seething energies. These individuals are often practitioners who do meridian body work with many clients and who have not understood how to protect themselves from the energy fields of others. They must spend more time clearing their fields before they can undertake the techniques described here and later, otherwise their assessments will be inaccurate. A field of conflicting energies and overcharge is as bad as one which is deficient in energies.

When we are in a relaxed state and the brain is in alpha rhythm, the heart becomes a resonating system allowing the body to resonate to the basic planetary frequency of about 8 hertz.[12] This is probably the reason why the speed of our recording arm as it tests ion flow corresponds with the heartbeat. Emotional conflict affects the heart and can cause us to break our connection with the health-giving energies of the earth. The many systems of meditation, psychological counselling and the exercises in this book restore this basic frequency and thus restore the rhythm of mother nature.

Our bodies require a balance of positive and negative ions for healthy electrical interplay. Pollutants in the environment such as lead, sulphur dioxide, and cadmium distort normal ion flow and cause a build up of carbon dioxide so that the oxygenation of our blood is diminished. Excess positive ions are caused by pollution, electrical and electronic machinery, smog, synthetic materials, hot winds, and heaters. Earthquakes, waterfalls, and post-thunder-storm conditions produce an excess of negative ions. As the atmosphere becomes disturbed by sunspot activity, earthquakes, volcanic eruptions and nuclear testing, it is useful to check the environment for ion flow on a regular basis in addition to that of our own body.

CHECKING FOR ENERGY OR ION FLOW

In the following exercise, we are using the arm as an instrument to record energy flow in any part of the body. It is important that the clearing exercises described in the first chapter (page 13) have been undertaken. It is also wise initially to do this new exercise in calm weather conditions and when our emotions are in a calm state. Following meditation would be an ideal time as our emotions have a profound effect on body energies but they are quiet after meditation. In this exercise you will aim to assess ion flow in all parts of the body.

1 Remove your watch and jewellery. A metal object or watch battery will change energy flows. Your clothing should be made of natural fibres and should be a light colour — definitely not black which negates the effect of light flow. Tight belts and ties should be removed.

2 Stand with your legs a bit apart and make sure your shoulders are down and relaxed with your arms held loosely at your side.

3 Test first one side of the body and then the other in the following manner. Place the tip of the middle finger very lightly on the part of the body you choose to be tested. Allow your mind to be as relaxed as possible. Allow your other recording hand to hang loosely at your side but make sure your sleeve is not touching your body as this short circuits the testing. It takes a bit of practice to hold the recording arm relaxed but in a slight curve so that it is not touching the body (see Diagram 5).

Diagram 5

RECORDING TECHNIQUES

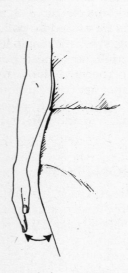

Record ion or horizontal flows with a back and forth movement—fingers are kept straight.

Testing for ion flow:
- Keep your shoulders down and relaxed.
- Recording arm must not touch body.
- Only the middle finger of the testing hand must touch your body.
- Arm should move gently back and forth.

The recording movement is denoted by a back and forth movement of the hand in response to whatever part of the body is touched by the middle finger on the other hand. Initially, before you become familiar with using your arm in this way, you may respond to the energy flow by feeling a tingling in your finger.

4 Use the middle finger of your right hand for touching and testing the right side of the body and the left middle finger for the left side. Do not cross the midline with the receiving finger.

5 To restore a balanced ion flow, exercise briefly and vigorously facing first approximately north and then south in stable weather conditions. Later, after having explored the material in chapter 6, you can also restore and enhance ion flow by exercising on the appropriate energy flow. The magnesium flow enhances negative ions and the phosphorus flow stimulates positive ions.

When you first practise recording ion flow and your arm moves back and forth, you may wonder if your imagination is working too hard! Alternatively, you may need to practise for about fifteen minutes on a number of days before any movement is noted. Some people take a while to learn to relax their arms and shoulders.

TESTING ION FLOW IN THE ENVIRONMENT

After becoming proficient at this testing, you will notice that in unsettled weather you will record a weaker ion flow when you are facing a particular direction. In this situation, a 'weak flow' means hardly any movement of the arm. Overall, it is preferable to have a slight predominance of negative ions in your body. We feel more energetic when there is a slight predominance of negative ions, and lethargic when there is an excess of positive ions.

As a general guide to your own flow balance stand in a north/south line facing north. If conditions are balanced, ion flow should be approximately the same on both sides of the body. This means that the right side of the body is facing east and the left faces west. Negative ions tend to come in from the north-west and positive ions from the south-east. So as we turn, we may find that the recording hand becomes weak when we face into a particular direction.

Usually, we feel very tired if the positive ions accumulate as they do in many buildings with airconditioning or heating. Test this fact by standing north/south in an overheated room and testing for ion flow. If the ions on the west side of the body are weak, this will prove to you that negative ions come in from the west. Go outside in the fresh air and exercise vigorously first facing north and then south. Then re-test ion flow on both sides of body while facing north/south and balance should be restored provided the atmosphere is balanced on that day.

Ion imbalances can disturb the entire lymphatic system. The antibodies of our immune system appear to be dependent on the regular exchange of energies between our Vivaxis (see chapter 5) and the receptor points for these energies on the body. It has been noted that epidemics and infections are more common after there has been a prolonged period of positive ions in the atmosphere.

Recording ion flow is a very accurate way to find energy blocks in the body without using any electronic gadgets. After you become accustomed to testing ion flow in your body using the method of touch, try scanning other objects in the environment with your eye but still using your recording hand. All our senses respond to energy flows. We started with touch because using a finger easily defines a particular area and is therefore very specific.

It is quicker to use the eye to scan a number of objects and especially if they are far off. You can start to check all the furniture and fittings in your home. Many soft furnishings will show lack of normal ion flow if they contain foam plastic or if the upholstery is made of synthetic material such as vinyl, nylon or acrylic. Note the amazing difference in recording energies between a tree or flower and a painted or plastic surface!

Inability to Record Energy Flows

There may be a number of reasons why you cannot record ion flow. If the clearing exercise has not been adequately performed, effects from X-rays may still be causing blocks in arms and shoulders. Sometimes there are energy blocks in the head which are partly caused by stress and negative emotions. These blocks often correspond with old injuries on the opposite side of the body. On occasions, a very persistent foreign field needs clearing over several weeks with the neutralising exercise described in chapter 1 (page 18).

If there are persistent difficulties, it may be necessary to seek the help of a practitioner in these sciences to help locate the difficulty. It is impossible to find a persistent foreign field unless you can test your energy flow, so such an individual is in a double bind. They will need to be helped by a trained person. However, less than ten per cent of people will have this as a continuing problem after carrying out the clearing exercises described earlier.

Diagnosing a Foreign Field

Whenever the recording hand registers a circulating movement while we are testing a certain place on the body, we will know that there is a disturbed wave in a horizontal direction. For a foreign field, there will also be a vertical wave which is linking part of the body with the foreign Vivaxis. To test for this vertical wave we hold the recording hand with our fingers pointed upwards (see Diagram 6). If we get a response in the recording hand we have recorded a foreign field provided it is combined with a disturbed horizontal wave.

Testing for Compatible Foods and Medicines

The ability to test energies by testing ion flow allows us to monitor energy flow in our own bodies, our environment, homes, cars, food and is an invaluable aid towards attaining health both at home and elsewhere. This technique can also be used for selecting appropriate food, remedies and their potency and dosage for self, family

Diagram 6

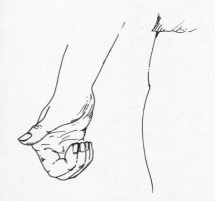

VERTICAL FLOW

Record a vertical flow with a back and forth movement—fingertips point upwards.

members and friends. The one golden rule to remember is that the mind and emotions must be neutral at the time of testing except for concentrating on the object or person concerned. The benefit of meditating to avoid influencing the ion test with your emotions and mind cannot be over-emphasised.

To test food for your own use, simply hold a sample in one hand and record the energies with the other. A normal strong ion flow while holding and concentrating on the sample will tell you that the food is compatible with your energy field. After some practice on food items, you can begin to test vitamins and minerals in the same way and also assess the dosage. When you go shopping or eat out in restaurants it is more appropriate to test by simply looking and observing the food and noting the reaction in your recording hand which is held quietly by your side.

3
PLANETARY CYCLES AND RHYTHMS

★ ★ ★ ★ ★ ★

*T*HE central theme of this book is earth energies but we cannot separate our planet from its interaction with other heavenly bodies and the electromagnetic effects they exert on our planet. There is also a strong gravitational effect from the moon which produces the tides. This gravitational pull varies during both the daily rotation of the earth and also during the earth's yearly passage around the sun.

SOME ASTRONOMICAL EFFECTS ON PLANETARY LIFE

The heavenly bodies and their effect on us have inspired the work not only of astrologers but of poets, musicians and philosophers throughout the ages. Even the conventional physicist, Isaac Newton, was a keen advocate of not only the laws pertaining to astronomy, but of astrology.

Astrology is sometimes considered a poor cousin to astronomy but scientific research is changing this perception. The French psychologist Michel Gauquelin and his wife investigated the birth charts of many thousands of individuals and established that particular planets were related to the prominent points or 'angles' of the birthchart in relation to both temperament and a successful profession or activity. The groups surveyed included leading athletes who were found to have a prominent Mars; scientists who had a prominent Saturn; medical people who had a prominent Saturn and Mars; poets and writers who had a prominent moon; and successful actors, politicians and diplomats who were found to have a prominent Jupiter.[1]

In relation to our subject of earth energies, these conditioning influences of the planets are found to be mainly focussed through the point of the zodiac on the eastern horizon at the time of birth – the traditional ascendant, and also at the point on the zodiac which is the highest point in the sky at the birth time. This is traditionally called the mid heaven and, except at the equator, it is never directly overhead. The angle of the equator to the ecliptic – which is the path of the earth around the sun – accounts for the twenty-four hours of darkness or light in extreme latitudes.

As the earth moves around the sun, different angular relationships are formed with each of the other planets which are pursuing their own orbital paths. Myriad patterns are formed which influence life on our earth. In the area of astronomy, scientific research has discovered that particular angular relationships between Mars, Saturn and Jupiter correspond with sunspot activity and epidemics.[2]

EARTH ROTATION AND DAILY RHYTHMS

The turning of the earth on its axis over twenty-four hours creates various bodily rhythms which are often referred to as circadian rhythms. These rhythms affect our sleeping patterns, eating habits and various glandular functions. Travelling long distances in a short time by air can profoundly affect our rhythms. At our new destination, we want to sleep during the day and we then often lie sleepless for many hours at night. In addition, we may wish to eat at strange times and our digestion can be impaired. Many women suffer menstrual irregularities when they travel. In short, the body clock becomes very disturbed.

The pineal gland is considered to be one of the main timekeepers in the body. It is also the director of the endocrine system. This means that the pineal regulates the other glands such as the pituitary, thyroid, thymus, pancreas, adrenals and gonads. The pineal gland is a tiny pine-cone shaped organ in the centre of the brain. One of the hormones it secretes is melatonin. The production of this hormone is stimulated by periods of light and darkness and, of course, when we travel the usual patterns are disturbed. Melatonin production peaks between 2 a.m. and 4 a.m., normally the darkest time during the twenty-four hour cycle.

Some people are very sensitive to changes in light intensity and they become severely depressed in winter. This problem is called Seasonal Affective Disorder (SAD). It can be alleviated by exposing the person to a strong full spectrum light each morning for an hour or so.[3] There have also been clinical trials conducted using medication with melatonin. The pineal secretes another hormone called serotonin which is needed for relaxation and perhaps this is one reason why travelling during the night can lead to trouble sleeping on subsequent nights.

One of the first discoveries about melatonin was its polarity with the gonadal hormones. Women with fertility problems were found to conceive if they slept in a lighted room during the time of ovulation. In other words, if there is an over-secretion of melatonin during the hours of darkness the function of the ovaries will be suppressed but light can be used to resolve the problem. It would be interesting to know if these women also suffered from depression.

In chapter 8, you will read how Fran Nixon discovered that the energy layers on the earth corresponding to the pineal gland frequency are active when the sun is near its meridian, that is, between the hours of 10 a.m. and 2 p.m. This may vary a little according to the latitude of the place on the planet. There are particular techniques using the frequencies from these energy bands to improve the health of the pineal. The pineal gland appears to be related to the reception of both physical and spiritual light and its health is important therefore in many respects. Not only is it affected by the cycle of day and night but possibly it reacts to the relationship between the sun, moon and earth.

The daily turning of the earth brings in energies which teachers of spiritual practices and meditation have known about for a long time. We have always been advised to meditate early in the morning as close to dawn as possible. It appears that a special energy flows towards us as the sun rises in the east. This subtle energy is quite different to the energy which comes from the heat of the sun when it is at the highest point in the sky. Many meditators have found there are three points of the day which are significant for meditation and these are dawn, midday and sunset. At each of these periods there are different types of energies available which are significant for our spiritual alignment.

THE RELATION OF SUN, MOON AND EARTH

The moon is the closest heavenly body to our planet and has the greatest gravitational effect manifesting as the ocean tides which occur during each twenty-four hour period. At the time of the new and full moon there are extra high and low tides – the spring tides. New and full moons occur when the moon, earth and sun form a straight line in terms of celestial longitude. Occasionally, the moon, earth, and sun will also be in the same latitude and this causes the moon to block out the light of the sun, or the sun to block out the light of the moon at that place on the planet where this exact alignment occurs. These phenomena are called eclipses of the sun or moon. An eclipse of the sun occurs when the moon comes between the earth and the sun at one of the new moons.

This temporary disappearance of light from the earth has always been seen by superstitious people to be a bad omen. It is understandable that the physical disappearance of light can come to symbolise the disappearance of spiritual light. It is interesting that there was an eclipse of the sun close to the beginning of the Gulf War in early 1991. This war was possibly the first war of aggression on our planet when almost all nations across the globe condemned the aggressor, Iraq. The world's reaction to the Gulf War could be considered as a milestone in a spiritual sense, despite some of the mixed motives in relation to oil supplies in the Middle East. So although the eclipse may have signified a disaster from many points of view, humanity behaved as a global village for the first time in recorded history.

If we analyse what may take place at these times of alignment between sun, moon and earth, we come to the following consideration. At the time of the new moon, the moon is between the earth and the sun and we would expect that the effect of the moon on the earth would be powerful in terms of its gravitational effect. As the sun symbolises spiritual light in all religions and cultures, the new moon could be interpreted as temporarily blocking out spiritual light on our planet. Thus it is the traditional time each month according to some cultures when evil can more easily take place. During an eclipse of the sun this effect from the moon is said to be enhanced.

With respect to more individual effects from the moon, I remember reading an account of some medical research which established that haemorrhage from surgery is far more likely to occur at the time of the full moon.[4] Perhaps the moon may have some extra gravitational effect at these times on bodily fluids which would affect the blood circulation. This effect has not yet been understood by medical science but we are not in danger because modern technology can usually deal with this tendency.

Another type of eclipse occurs when the earth comes between the sun and the moon at one of the full moons. In astronomical terms, this means that the moon is on the opposite side of the earth from the sun, thus blocking out the light of the moon on one side of the earth. Again, this is caused by alignment in both longitude and latitude of the sun, moon, and earth. As this phenomenon does not cause any disappearance of sunlight it is not viewed traditionally as a dangerous time.

Indeed, over the period of the full moon during the monthly alignment between the sun, earth and moon we can experience a deeper and closer alignment with spiritual levels. It is an opportunity to access energies from the particular constellation behind the sun for the healing of ourselves, the planet and the kingdoms in nature. In this process, the moon reflects the energies from the sun and constellation behind back to the earth, rather than transmitting its own energies.

In contrast to the other planets in our solar system, the moon is considered to be a dead and disintegrating planet which only shines from the reflected light of the sun. In the ancient wisdom teachings, each of the main planets are considered as the physical body of a great intelligence but not the moon.[5]

During the course of the year we have an opportunity to receive energy from each of the twelve signs of the zodiac as the earth moves around the sun. These energies are experienced more fully when we meditate as a group because this provides a stronger channel. The other advantage of a group meditation is to protect the individual from the powerful energies contacted. The full moon each month is celebrated as a spiritual festival by many individuals and groups throughout the world.

The Buddhist religion celebrates the Wesak festival held at the full moon of May, often called the full moon of Taurus because that is the constellation in line with the sun at this time. This festival is also the high point for a large group of Westerners who gather together at this time of the year with the aim of transmitting spiritual energies into our planet. Alice Bailey is one writer who has written extensively on this full moon approach as a means to align with the spiritual Hierarchy or inner teachers in the subjective planetary realms.[6]

In Celtic culture, May day was a special time when the fertility of the earth was celebrated in a pagan rite which seemed to be a sexual orgy for all concerned. The aim was to transmit this human expression of fecundity into the earth for the promotion of life-giving crops. Perhaps the original spiritual impulse of this Celtic expression lost its true significance and degenerated over the centuries.

THE EFFECT OF THE TIDES ON OUR ENERGIES

Each day as the earth turns on its axis there is the smaller cycle involving the alignment between sun, moon and earth which causes the daily tides. There are roughly two high tides and two low tides each twenty-four hours. The high tides occur when the moon is directly over a particular place and also when it is on the opposite side of the earth, both being caused by the daily rotation of the earth. At the time of the two daily low tides, the moon is at right angles to that position on the earth and is therefore found on the east or west horizon of the place in question.

At the full and new moons there are extra high tides (spring tides). Extra low tides or neap tides occur when the sun and moon are at right angles to each other which is the same as the low daily tides mentioned above. The difference between the daily and monthly tides is that the former are caused by the rotation of the earth and the latter by the passage of the moon around the earth.

An experiment on the effect of the tides on the vegetable kingdom was conducted by medical scientist H. S. Burr over a thirty-year period. He attached electrodes to the cambium or living layer of tree trunks on his own property in Connecticut, USA. His research was designed to show the effects of planetary rhythms on the life fields (L-fields).[7]

Burr established that both the turning of the earth on its axis, new and full moons, and the seasons as the earth circled the sun had a definite effect on the electromagnetic or L-field of his trees. The L-field fluctuated in intensity with these planetary movements. It would be difficult to wire up humans in such a continuous way but if one kingdom in nature is affected in this way, the inference is that all kingdoms of nature would show effects from the moon cycle.

Another example of the effect of tides on living creatures was established long ago by scientists working on oysters. The oysters were taken from their home and transported thousands of miles away and after a few weeks they changed the opening times of their shells to coincide with their new position.[8] In other words, at their new location they had become adjusted to the alignment between sun, moon and earth. This indicates the gravitational effect of the moon on living creatures even when far away from the sea and not directly subject to the movement of the tides.

The smaller cycle of the daily tides can also be used for spiritual purposes and for meditation. In keeping with the experience of meditators that sunrise and sunset are powerful times for meditation, the low tides when the moon is on the horizon are also powerful times for meditation, aiding alignment and spiritual penetration. Unfortunately, the tides are one hour later each day which means that we cannot meditate with the low tide at the same time each day. However every twelve days or so, the low tide will correspond with sunrise and sunset and this is especially powerful for sun and moon are then in an alignment on our planetary horizon.

My work with Fran Nixon indicated a practical reason why the planetary movements may have an effect on our consciousness. Fran found that creative thought was stimulated by receptors on the body which are associated with the vertical vector or direction of the element chromium. There are horizontal and vertical vectors for most of the elements in our bodies. The word vector is used because as well as meaning a direction it denotes force and velocity. However, for the sake of simplicity in this book, I have mainly used the terms flow, wave or direction instead of vector.

At the time of the full and new moons and also at the high and low tides, many of the receptors for elements on the body become quiescent.[9] However, the vertical chromium receptors are more powerful at high and low tides and perhaps are the physical means whereby a connection is made with higher levels of manifestation.

In addition, and perhaps more importantly, Fran found that the angular or mathematical relationship between the three celestial bodies of sun, moon and earth is reflected in the spinal canal of our body between the level of the navel and the thymus gland. At the high tides, the vectors of light accompanying this phenomenon are found to come into our spine in a vertical direction, and at the low tides the light vectors are at right angles.

In many spiritual disciplines, the subtle channels associated with the spine are considered to house energy flows which are directly related to our spiritual growth and practice. There are three channels in eastern philosophy – Ida, Pingala and Sushumna. One is masculine, one feminine and the central channel, Sushumna, is androgynous. These channels are connected with the energy centres or chakras which we discuss in chapter 8.

As the energy centres become active and purified, the energies in the spinal channels rise upwards towards the head. These subtle spinal canals and currents connect with endocrine glands in the head via the two head chakras. The pituitary gland is connected with the feminine channel which in turn connects with the two chakras concerned with our creative life, the sacral and throat chakras. The masculine channel responds to two other chakras, the solar plexus and heart. The central channel is related to the base and crown chakras which are the last pair to become active.

The third eye develops from the union of the magnetic fields around the pituitary and pineal glands. This relation of the pituitary gland to the pineal takes place at a stage in our spiritual life when the energies are able to travel freely up the spinal channels. This coincides with an opening and alignment between all the chakras or energy centres. In a psycho-spiritual sense it relates to the alignment between our integrated personality and our soul or inner essence. This is termed the true marriage in heaven and allows us to experience heaven on earth.

At the high and low tides and at the new and full moons, the gravitational influence of the sun and moon may affect the fluids in our spine which in turn must influence the more subtle energy currents in our spinal channels. I have noticed that meditation is usually most powerful at low tide. In many cases I have tested this after meditation and therefore was not expecting the extra stimulation at the time of sitting down to meditate. Don't forget that the tides are one hour later each day so we cannot always keep these special times. However, it is very useful to know how to anticipate these tidal cycles. I learnt a technique from Fran Nixon which is invaluable for finding the exact position of the tides without reference to any external tables or charts.

Fran called this technique 'finding the solunar flow'. The solunar flow denotes that period of time between the high and low tides which lasts for approximately six hours. The times of the tides have always been used by fishermen to ascertain the times when fish are most likely to bite. It was a fairly simple procedure during holidays by the sea to check the technique developed by Fran with the tables which are in most local papers. Fran referred to the low tide as the minor period and this lasts for about twenty minutes. She referred to high tide as the major period and this lasts for over an hour.

These rhythms can be accurately found on the body no matter how far away we are from the ocean.

Before describing this technique, you need to establish the correct finger to use for testing. In this exercise we do not use the middle or ion flow finger. Once established, the same finger will be used for all testing above the waist. You should use either the index or ring finger depending on whether you are above or below your Vivaxis in terms of altitude. If above the Vivaxis, the index finger will be the recording finger and if below it will be the ring finger. Remember that to test ion flow you used the middle finger and this finger is always used for ion testing regardless of our location.

Until the method for finding whether you are above or below your Vivaxis is described, the simplest approach is to try first the index and then the ring finger of the left hand until a response is obtained in your recording hand. The left hand is used because the flow of our Vivaxis energies is received via left leg and arm.

TECHNIQUES FOR FINDING THE TIDES AND SOLUNAR FLOWS PERIODS

METHOD 1

The gravitational influences of the sun and moon travel up and down a 1.28 cm wide ($1/2$ inch) band which Fran Nixon called the solunar flow tract. It is located in a straight line from the navel to the notch on the front of the body just below the meeting point of the clavicles (shoulder girdle). This slight hollow is over the thymus gland. The top of the tract registers energy at the major period which corresponds with high tide and the section at the navel corresponds to the minor period or low tide (see Diagram 7). As the terms major and minor period are not in universal usage, I will mainly use the terms high and low tide.

1 Check ion flow to establish that it is reasonably balanced as you face the four quadrants of the compass. If necessary, balance your ion flow before locating the solunar flow. Face in a westerly direction and think of or concentrate on the sun. (I do not know why the sun relates to the west and the moon to the south but practical experience validates these directions. In other words, if you face west and concentrate on the moon, your recording arm will not respond. Conversely, if you face south and record the movement of the moon, your recording arm will cut out as soon as you concentrate on the sun!)

Diagram 7

DETERMINING SOLUNAR FLOW AND HIGH AND LOW TIDE

The cycle of high and low tides and the period in-between called the solunar flow period registers on the solunar tract.

2 Place the tip of your testing finger (either the index or ring finger of your left hand) lightly on top of the tract. Hold the other hand ready for recording (slightly away from the body and with fingers relaxed but extended).

3 Move your testing finger in small jumps gradually down the tract. Do not drag your finger as this causes static on the surface of the body. It is also important not to press too hard; in fact you can perform this test with your finger not quite touching your body as you are measuring subtle energies. At some point along the tract, your recording hand will start to move. Stop moving your finger at this point and wait about thirty seconds. After some seconds your recording hand will cease its motion. This is because the spine has already recorded a slight change in the position of the tide.

4 Now you need to find out whether there is a movement towards high or low tide. Move your testing finger on slightly to deter-mine the new position. As the flow may be going up or down at the time of testing, you may have to move your finger either up or down the solunar tract to relocate the new tide position. We can thus ascertain whether we are moving towards high or low tide. The point on the solunar tract where the flow is recorded at

any point of time gives us an approximate time between the high and low tide, that is, how far we are into the solunar flow period.

5 Some people may find it easier to concentrate on the moon instead of the sun but in this case they need to face south while doing the exercise. The directions of west and south are related to the positions of the sun and moon as they are received by the body. If an individual tries facing directions other than south or west while testing, a slightly different position on the body for the tide flows will be recorded and this will be less accurate. Presumably this relates to the fact that the angular relationship of the sun and moon to the earth in some way relates to west and south.

6 It may be important to find how long before a high or low tide finishes. For evaluating the time left in a high tide, keep your testing finger on the notch in front of the thymus and tilt your head slowly backwards. At a particular angle of the head tilt, the recording arm will cut out. Roughly divide this angle or space into the full head-tilting angle. The total angle represents eighty minutes. If your head is tilted half-way back from level to its full extension and the recording stops, you would halve eighty minutes.

For the low tide, the head is tilted downwards until the recording arm cuts out and the same calculation is made but remembering that the minor period or low tide only lasts twenty minutes. For example, if your head is tilted half-way from level down to the chest when the recording arm stops, we know that half of the minor period is gone which is half of twenty minutes, i.e. ten minutes.

METHOD 2

The gravitational energies of the sun travel behind the right ear in an arc on the mastoid bone, while those of the moon travel behind the left ear. In testing the tides using your ears, the position of the high and low tides is reversed from the position on the spine, with the major period or high tide being found at the bottom of the ear, and the minor period or low tide at the top of the ear.

1 As with Method 1, check your ion flow. If using your right ear, face in a westerly direction and concentrate on the sun. Place the tip of your testing finger on the mastoid bone and move in small jumps in an arc from the bottom to the top of the ear. Record the exact position of the tide in the same way as Method 1.

If you prefer to use your left ear, face south and concentrate on the moon while using your testing finger to move over the mastoid bone in the same way as you did with the right ear. The same technique for finding the distance into a major or minor period is used as for Method 1.

In working with students, I find Method 2 can be problematic because so many people have a history of ear problems which seem to affect the recording of energies on this part of the body. Also, it is a very small area whereas the tract between thymus and navel allows for greater differentiation. There can be difficulties using Method 1 however if there is a history of spinal problems, so it is appropriate that we have a choice of two methods.

The importance of working with the tides will become more obvious later when we look at the various types of mineral and energy flows on the body. At the high and low tides, some of these energy flows disappear until the solunar flow resumes. This means that we cannot work with those energies at the times of high and low tides. I have discovered that the same phenomenon takes place at the new and full moon, but it lasts much longer. At these times, a number of energy flows disappear for four hours before and afterwards.

This phenomenon may account for why some people are imbalanced at the time of the full moon. For instance, if you are very short of the minerals which coincide with those frequencies which disappear, you may feel more disturbed than those individuals who have a plentiful supply. One example here may relate to chromium which contributes to the regulation of blood sugar by the pancreas. It is possible that some people are more likely to suffer hypoglycaemia or low blood sugar at the new and full moons and at the high and low tides. The mineral zinc could also be implicated in this way. Homeopaths have consistently noticed that people with an imbalance of the element silica are worse at the new moon.

Finding the position of the tides is not only useful for enhancing meditation but also for very practical issues involving the best times to tap into the frequencies of different minerals which are basic for health.

4

THE VIBRATORY DANCE OF THE ELEMENTS

★ ★ ★ ★ ★ ★

ONE of the most exciting advances in natural medicine is the information we are gathering about the vibratory frequencies important for life. It is becoming apparent that good health is achieved by restoring the right frequencies to different parts of the body. Eventually we will know exactly what sound, colour, mineral, herb, homeopathic or flower essence will rebalance our body frequencies. The appropriate remedy will match the disease state and will therefore help restore the individual to health and harmony.

The frequencies of the elements in the periodic table have already been established by science. Each element emits a certain frequency which is linked to the atomic weight of that element. In this chapter, we will be working and acquainting ourselves with the exact frequencies needed for health and finding receptors for these elements on our body.

LIFE FREQUENCIES AND OUR HEALTH

Our bodies contain all those elements in the periodic table which are essential for health and life – hydrogen, oxygen, nitrogen, carbon, calcium, sodium, magnesium, sulphur, potassium, chlorine, fluorine, phosphorus and so on. Of course, there are also many elements on our planet which are harmful in any but minute quantities. Examples of injurious elements are lead, cadmium, and mercury.

Fran Nixon discovered that there are receptors for all the life-giving elements throughout the body. Many key receptors are on the fingers, toes, and around the eyes and head. She found that these receptors are concerned with transmitting energy from one part of the body to another, and are connected with the movement of any part of the body. In every case of paralysis or impediment to normal movements she found associated disturbed receptors on the head, fingers and toes.

Chinese medicine established the teaching thousands of years ago that energy in the body runs in circuits called meridians. There are twelve classical meridians and many other subsidiary meridians which have been the subject of research more recently. Acupuncture points on each meridian have a lower electrical resistance than the surrounding skin area. These points have now been charted by simple physical instruments which measure skin resistance. The points are used by acupuncturists to link one meridian with another for the purpose of rebalancing the energies of the body. For instance, if the liver is found to be congested with too much energy, acupuncture needles will be placed so as to drain off excess liver energy to another organ which, in contrast, may be depleted.

Although Fran Nixon had absolutely no knowledge of acupuncture, scientists established that many of the points on the body which she called receptors are in fact acupuncture points. Nor is it surprising that she found minerals associated with the receptors because minerals are necessary to carry an electrical current – even the tiny currents associated with the physical body. I have found that some individuals respond better to acupuncture than others and consider the response to be partly related to the mineral status in their body.

However, the body can only absorb minerals in a very assimilable form, either through the plant kingdom which is the correct food and medicine for humanity, or through colloidal preparation where the minerals are in a very fine suspension. Minerals are the basic building blocks of the cells and so their presence in the body in the correct balance and frequency is very important for health.

As we shall discover shortly, we can also obtain these frequencies directly from planet Earth which is still cheaper and easier. We do this by aligning ourselves with the energy bands or layers which exist throughout the earth and which are detailed in the next chapter. First, however, we need to become familiar with charting the minerals on our own body. It is appropriate and useful to start with our hands.[1]

THE MINERAL FREQUENCIES ON OUR HANDS

Having learnt how to undertake testing for ion flow, we are in a position to test for any of the minerals associated with our body. We need to have cleared our circuits (see page 10) and to have established that we are in a solunar flow period which is the time between high and low tide. It is during this approximately six-hour period that all the elemental frequencies are present and in a balanced state and therefore that is the time we do most testing and correcting of energy flows.

To be able to check the receptor points of elements on our bodies we must learn to visualise each substance clearly in our mind. It is useful to build up a collection of samples for this purpose. To start with one of the most important elements, purchase a small amount of chromium oxide which should be available from any ceramic or potters' supplier. The chromium oxide powder is grass green in colour. It is essential for you to register this frequency in your brain because you will need to visualise chromium when you are looking for the energy layers. Once you can visualise a substance in its material form, you can usually recall the vibration just by thinking of the original sample. It is not always necessary to have the sample visible when testing.

Readers will be familiar with the frequencies of many elements in the course of daily living. For instance, we have all seen copper pipes or kettles, iron nails, chalk (calcium) and salt (sodium). Other substances such as iodine or zinc can be purchased from the chemist and the rarer elements, such as selenium, can be obtained from chemical suppliers. Some elements can be obtained from vitamin and health-food stores; magnesium for example is available in the form of magnesium oxide or orotate. It is necessary to buy tablets which are not combined with other vitamins and minerals to avoid confusion when absorbing a particular wavelength.

Once we learn to pick up mineral frequencies on our bodies, we are on the way to a whole new life adventure where we can visualise and diagnose the frequencies of anything on our planet, and test whether these elements are compatible to our well-being. I have found over the years that people learn about frequencies most quickly by starting with those frequencies that are present on our own bodies.

The Technique for Finding the Mineral Frequencies

1 Turn one hand palm up a comfortable distance from your eyes and look at the centre of the fingertip on your middle finger. Visualise chromium oxide on this point and hold your other hand in the position for recording ion flow to record the presence of chromium. The fingers of your recording hand should be straight. This is the position in which we hold the hand when recording the horizontal flow of an element.

  If there is no response, keep the recording hand in the same position but with the fingertips curled upwards, pointing towards the sky (see Diagram 6). This position records a vertical flow. On one hand the horizontal chromium receptors will be on the front of the finger (finger pad) and on the other hand it will be a vertical flow on the finger pad. The back of your fingers (fingernail) will record the opposite, that is, if the horizontal flow is on the front, the flow on the back will be vertical.

  Now that you have established where the vertical and horizontal chromium receptors are situated, you can move on to looking for other elements on your other fingers. The index and ring fingers are a little more complicated because they may have receptors for any one of three elements.

2 Everyone has the iron frequency receptors on both hands on either index or ring finger and the position is reversed from hand to hand. For instance, if you have iron on the index finger of your right hand it will be on the ring finger of the left hand. Usually the horizontal flows are on the pads of these fingers and the vertical flows on the back. Use the same techniques for visualising and testing for iron as you have already done for chromium.

  Test both index and ring fingers first for horizontal flows of iron by visualising iron on your finger pad (think of iron nails) and if it is not present then test for a vertical flow visualising iron while holding the recording hand in the vertical position. Having discovered which finger on each hand has the frequency for iron, we can consider the remaining index and ring fingers. It is helpful to make a chart as you go through these tests (see Diagram 8).

3 The remaining index and ring fingers will either be zinc or iodine depending on the individual. It is still a mystery as to why some

Diagram 8

GROUPS OF ELEMENTS IN CENTRE OF FINGER PADS

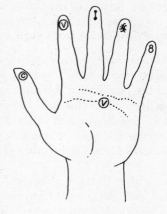 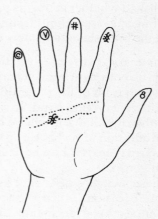

©	copper	✗	magnetic group
Ⓥ	gravitational group	8	selenium
↕	vertical chromium	#	horizontal chromium

people are iodine people and some zinc but it may have something to do with the associated endocrine glands. Zinc is associated with the gonads – ovaries and testes – and iodine is associated with the thyroid. Over many years of teaching these techniques I can often tell which mineral a person has by their personality and body type.

The 'zinc' type is more common. People with zinc receptors on the fingers appear to have a stronger type of constitution. The 'iodine' person is more mentally active. These types will become more meaningful when we look at the chakras or energy centres later in the book. Test first for zinc by visualising zinc cream on your fingers, and if there is no response, visualise iodine.

4 This leaves the thumb and little finger and they are associated with the elements copper and selenium. If the right thumb pad has selenium, the left thumb will have copper. The positions on the other hand will be reversed. This means the right little finger will have copper and the left little finger will have selenium. Repeat the procedure as for the other elements visualising first copper and then selenium on the centre of the thumb pad. You

will probably have to purchase a small amount of selenium from a chemical company to help you with that visualisation as most selenium tablets are mixed with other ingredients. Once you have established whether copper is present on the pad of the thumb or little finger, even without testing, you can assume selenium will be on the opposite of whatever copper is on.

In summary, everyone has horizontal and vertical pairs of elements on both right and left hands. The direction of flow reverses from back to front of the fingertip and the position of the minerals is also different on each hand. To repeat, if iron is on the index finger pad on the right hand it will be on the ring finger pad of the left hand. In addition, if we have iron with a vertical flow on one side of the fingertip there will be a horizontal flow of iron on the other side of the fingertip.

All these switches of energy keep us alert as to our recording. There are occasions when the vertical and horizontal chromium groups appear to be together on the same side of the finger and that occurs if we are facing our Vivaxis or standing in the energy layers. In these positions gravitational and magnetic waves, as Fran called them, are moving in a parallel direction. In other positions, they are at right angles to each other just as they are around an electric wire.

When visualising the elements it makes it easier if you imagine that the element is actually on your finger. This prevents you from keeping the awareness of the vibration or frequency only in your brain. Some people are more gifted with visualising than others but I have rarely found anyone who was unable to test the elements on the fingertips.

It is not uncommon for a person to have difficulty finding a mineral if their body is deficient in that mineral. I can recall that in one of my seminars a woman was unable to find iron because she had a tendency to anaemia. She was more successful in this task when we had helped her to 'channel' iron from the appropriate layer of the energy flows. Many people are deficient in zinc and selenium and others may need supplementation with chromium and iodine.

The exact position of the receptor is in the centre of the whorl on the fingertip. When you look closely at your hand you can see it is covered in fine lines which are called the dermatoglyphics. On the fingertips these lines usually form a loop, or a tent or, more uncommonly, a small whorl pattern. It is not necessary to be looking at this exact spot when testing; just look approximately at the centre of your fingertip.

The visualisation of the central element on the fingertip is important because there are other minerals which are individual for each person arranged around the central mineral. The visualisation process involving a particular element allows us to concentrate on that element and this concentration automatically blocks out other frequencies from our awareness.

Our receptors are in constant use in daily life absorbing frequencies from the environment. Later on, we will learn how these receptors can receive balancing doses of the relevant frequency from the energy flows.

FINDING THE TESTING FINGER BY EVALUATING THE ENERGY SKIRT

We now need to ascertain which finger we should use as the testing finger because many of the procedures which follow require the use of the correct testing finger. The testing finger will be the ring or index finger of the left hand because our Vivaxis energies flow in a vertical direction towards us via the left foot and hand and out the other hand and foot. If we are above our Vivaxis the testing finger will be the index finger for testing areas above the waist such as the solunar flow tract. If we are below our Vivaxis, the recording finger will be the ring finger for testing areas above the waist. The choice of fingers is related to the elements on our fingers and their correspondence to the elements in our auric layers or energy skirt.[2]

To find the testing finger is easier than may be imagined and does not entail finding the Vivaxis itself. It is also a very interesting exercise for other reasons as it enables us to test the size of our energy field at any point of time. Diagram 9 shows the general structure of the aura and its two main energy layers – the magnetic and gravitational.

Our energy field has an inner and an outer layer and these layers correspond to two of the force flows in the energy layers on the earth with which we will shortly be working. If we are above our Vivaxis, the outer layer will be the magnetic layer and the inner will be the gravitational. If below the Vivaxis, the positions will be reversed. The magnetic layer has iron as the central element and we have already found this on two of our fingers. The gravitational layer has either iodine or zinc as its main group and we have also found one of these elements on our fingers. So we are in a position now to visualise these elements in our energy skirt.[3]

Diagram 9

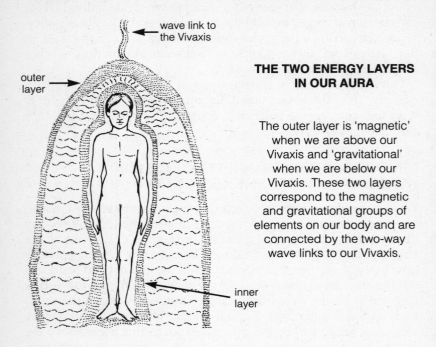

wave link to
the Vivaxis

outer
layer

THE TWO ENERGY LAYERS
IN OUR AURA

The outer layer is 'magnetic'
when we are above our
Vivaxis and 'gravitational'
when we are below our
Vivaxis. These two layers
correspond to the magnetic
and gravitational groups of
elements on our body and are
connected by the two-way
wave links to our Vivaxis.

inner
layer

When the outer layer of our aura contains the magnetic frequencies such as iron, the receptor on the left index finger will respond to the iron frequency and this will be the recording finger for all testing above the waist, apart from when we test ion flow. The sort of testing you can do with this finger will include testing receptors and also finding solunar flow. With the magnetic band as the outside layer of our energy field, the right hand will have the opposite arrangement with the iron frequency on the right ring finger.

If we are below our Vivaxis, there is a reversal of all these positions. The gravitational band containing the frequency of iodine or zinc will now be the outer band on the energy skirt and we will find a reversal of positions on the fingers and the left ring finger will respond to the iron or magnetic frequency, and will be the testing finger for above the waist and the right index finger will now contain the iron frequency.

To find which is the outer layer, think of one of the magnetic elements such as iron or copper. While visualising this element gradually move the fingertips of your left hand out horizontally from your body. When your fingertips touch the outer band there will be a response in your recording arm. If the magnetic band is on the outside, we know we are above our Vivaxis and that the inner band is the gravitational one.

If your recording arm does not respond when you visualise iron, repeat the procedure concentrating on iodine or zinc depending on which of these elements you found on your hands during the previous exercises. If you get a response to iodine or zinc, you will know that you are below your Vivaxis. It is interesting to test the size of your energy field when tired and then again when you feel filled with energy after channelling or meditating. In other words, how far outwards do you stretch your arm before you touch the outer layer of the energy field?

It is the area between these two layers in which we hold our recording hands for all the testing procedures. Unfortunately, if a person is in a very depleted state, they may not be able to test anything because their energy layers will be too close to the body. We will not worry about the opposite and unlikely possibility that a person has such an enormous energy field they cannot reach the outer band with their recording hand! Such an occurrence can happen after channelling but otherwise your fingertips will touch the outer rim before your arm is quite straight.

In summary, when you are above your Vivaxis, use the left-hand index finger when testing areas of the body above the navel, and the left-hand ring finger when testing areas below the waist. When below the Vivaxis the sequence is reversed; use the left-hand ring finger for testing above the navel and left-hand index finger for testing below the navel. The middle finger is used for testing ion flow no matter what our position.

THE TRIPLE GROUPS ON THE BODY

The elements on your fingertips are part of a triple group system which is found throughout the cranium and skeleton. The groups are called triple groups because they contain three receptors clustered together. Later, you will use these groups on your fingers and legs to help find your Vivaxis as detailed (see chapter 5). In the meantime, you can find one of the many triple groups of elements in the centre line of your forehead just below the hair-line. This will be a chromium group and you need to test whether the top receptor is chromium vertical or horizontal.[4] The horizontal

Diagram 10

THE TRIPLE VIVAXIS GROUPS

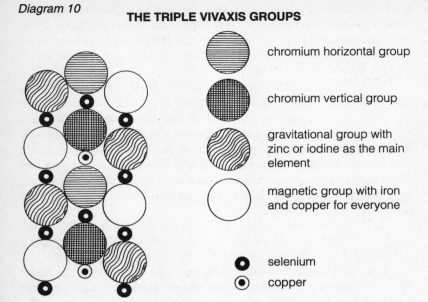

chromium horizontal group

chromium vertical group

gravitational group with zinc or iodine as the main element

magnetic group with iron and copper for everyone

selenium

copper

chromium groups will alternate with the vertical as you lightly move the testing finger down the midline.

On either side of the chromium group on the forehead there is a line of receptors relating to the other elements on the fingers – iron and zinc, or iron and iodine. As you can see in Diagram 10, selenium and copper groups also feature between each of these groups. Each magnetic group (iron) and gravitational group (iodine or zinc) will have horizontal waves on the front of the body with vertical waves on the back or the reverse, depending on whether we are above or below the Vivaxis. This arrangement corresponds to the location of the vertical and horizontal waves on the fingers.

In addition, the triple groups will be found to have alternating left and right hand spin as you go down the line. All of this sounds very complicated until you have done it a few times and then the amazing symmetry and consistency of these various energy flows is experienced.

Testing the Triple Groups

1 Start by testing groups on the front and back of your head. Touch the centre line of your forehead with the appropriate testing finger just below the hairline while holding your recording hand

for a horizontal flow and visualise chromium oxide (see Diagram 11a). If there is no response, hold your recording hand for a vertical flow.

2 Move your finger slightly down your forehead and repeat, noting that if the previous flow was vertical, the next will be horizontal. Move down and repeat the procedure a few more times.

3 Move your testing finger slightly to one side of the midline and find an iron group by visualising iron and testing for horizontal or vertical flow. When you have established whether the iron flow is vertical or horizontal remember that all the energy flows on the front of the body will be the same except for the chromium groups which contain both horizontal and vertical flows.

4 Move your testing finger down a bit further and visualise the other mineral previously found on your fingers – iodine or zinc. Continue moving down the same line and experience that the iron alternates with iodine or zinc.

5 Now move your testing finger to the back of your head and find a point slightly to either side of the midline. Move your finger down until you find an iron group. Note that the energy flow will be different from the flow on the forehead, that is, if a vertical flow is found on the forehead the flow will be horizontal on the back of the head. You can continue moving down the back of your head and find the other mineral groups containing zinc or iodine and chromium (see Diagram 11b).

6 Now come back to your forehead and test for the reverse spin of the groups as you move down the line of minerals. Curl the fingers of your recording hand and hold your hand horizontal with your thumb pointing upwards as in Diagram 11c. Move your testing finger slowly down a line of groups noting how the successive groups have an opposite spin from the one before. In other words, your recording hand will move in a circle first one way (e.g. clockwise) and then the other way with the next group down.

THE DISCOVERY AND DESCRIPTION OF THE ENERGY LAYERS

The skills learnt in visualising and testing the elements on the body can now be transferred to the exciting task of finding the energy layers associated with our Vivaxis.[5] These layers contain the

Diagram 11

TESTING HORIZONTAL AND VERTICAL CHROMIUM

(A)   (B)   (C)

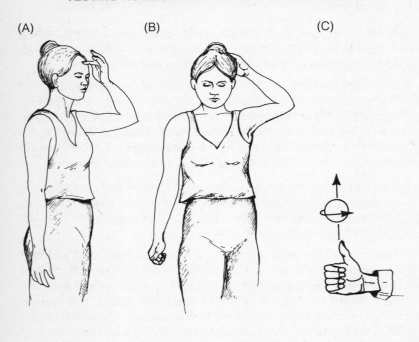

(A) Hand position for testing a horizontal group—visualise chromium and use your middle finger as it has the chromium receptors on the finger pad.

(B) Hand position for testing a verticall group on the back of the head—fingers of recording hand point upwards.

(C) Position of hand to test for direction of spin.

frequencies of our Vivaxis and we can only test them in a solunar flow period during which time all the elements are active and flowing back and forth between our Vivaxis and body.

Having established that we can test the vibratory frequency of various elements on our bodies, we are in a position to find the energy layers on the ground. It is here that we can really appreciate the healing properties of our earth. As with many of her discoveries,

Fran with her lateral thinking appeared to come upon the phenomenon of energy layers by chance. She was testing the direction of
flow from a chromium receptor on her head and she noted that it
appeared to flow towards a particular spot higher on the cabin wall.
Later it was established that this was the nearest energy layer to the
top of her head and that she was attracted to the chromium flow in
that particular layer.

From that point of time on, she and her colleague, a research
chemist, systematically mapped out all the known frequencies for
life on the energy layers. When they had finished there was a band
marked some 41 cm (16 inches) deep in cross section. Further bands
were added over the next few years as the science progressed (see
Diagram 12).

The bands or, more correctly, layers of energy are found running
continuously over the surface of the earth like the skins of an onion.
If we place a huge rod in the ground pointing towards the centre of
the earth, the distance between the layers will be 2.5–3.5 metres
(about 8–12 feet) depending on the location. Like most phenomena
to do with vibration and frequency, the layers over a distance are
undulating in keeping with all wave phenomena. This may be the
reason why in some places the distance between layers varies.

If we are walking up a hill, depending on the steepness of the hill,
we will cross a new layer every ten to fifteen steps depending on the
degree of the slope and size of our steps. The reader will realise that
the undulations, hills and mountains on our planet cut through
these layers; in other words they do not follow the contours of the
land. We can therefore locate the layers on any suitable vertical
surface (e.g. a tree) and you will find they occur at intervals of about
every 3 metres (9 feet). Of course the layers will continue into the
space either side of the vertical surface (tree, wall, hill). No doubt
many of the benefits of bushwalking relate to the effects of walking
across these energy layers (see Diagram 13).

Each complete layer is about 41 cm (16 inches) deep and consists
of a number of force flows.[6] There are four main force flows in each
complete layer and a number of other flows which with the central
four make ten flows altogether. Each force flow emits particular
frequencies which are associated with key elements essential for
life. The upper and lower boundaries have been named upper and
lower whites and these flows of energy relate to the pineal gland.
These white flows are only present between 10 a.m. and 2 p.m.
when there is maximum light coming from the sun.

Moving down the layer, we next find a flow associated with the

Diagram 12

CROSS-SECTION OF FORCE FLOWS WITH MAIN ELEMENTS

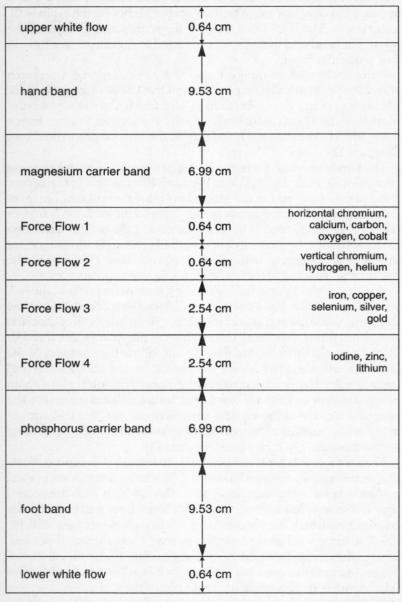

upper white flow	0.64 cm	
hand band	9.53 cm	
magnesium carrier band	6.99 cm	
Force Flow 1	0.64 cm	horizontal chromium, calcium, carbon, oxygen, cobalt
Force Flow 2	0.64 cm	vertical chromium, hydrogen, helium
Force Flow 3	2.54 cm	iron, copper, selenium, silver, gold
Force Flow 4	2.54 cm	iodine, zinc, lithium
phosphorus carrier band	6.99 cm	
foot band	9.53 cm	
lower white flow	0.64 cm	

not to scale

Diagram 13

THE ENERGY LAYERS DEPICTED ON A HILL AND A TREE

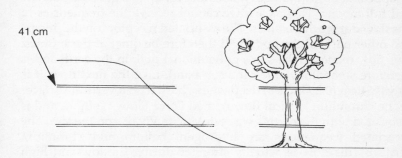

41 cm

Diagram 14

THE EFFECT OF GRADIENT ON MARKING THE ENERGY LAYERS

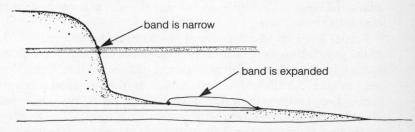

band is narrow

band is expanded

The energy layers are spread out and easier to mark on a gentle slope.

hand – this flow is 9.53 cm (about 3 inches) deep. There is a section on this flow for each of the five fingers and this part of the layer can be used for disturbances in the hand such as static, disturbed receptors on the hand, and for medical conditions such as arthritis in the hands.

The next force flow down is associated with magnesium and Fran called this a carrier band because it also carries the frequencies of other elements apart from magnesium. Magnesium is a most important mineral in the body and in my twenty-five years of naturopathic practice, I have used more magnesium compounds for clients than any other. This band is 6.99 cm (2.75 inches) deep. The magnesium force flow is also associated with negative ions.

Moving further down we then come to the chromium horizontal flow which Fran named Force Flow 1; perhaps because she discovered it first but also because it is the means whereby we locate the energy layers. This flow includes frequencies of chromium, oxygen, carbon, cobalt and calcium. It is one of the two flows which disappear at the low and high tides and for up to eight hours at new and full moons. This means we cannot receive the frequencies of this flow during those times. The associated receptors on the fingers and other parts of the body will therefore be quiet at these times. This flow relates to the sun's gravitational pull on the earth and is therefore sometimes called the sun band. Like the next flow, it is only 0.64 cm (0.25 inches) deep when charted on a vertical surface.

The chromium vertical flow named Force Flow 2 follows and is associated with the earth's wave link to its Vivaxis on the sun. The associated frequencies are hydrogen, helium and chromium vertical. This flow is actually stronger during the low and high tides. Probably its relation to the sun is the reason why meditation and creative thought appears stronger at this time. It could be that this vertical wave relates to our spiritual alignment with higher planes of being. We are reminded that the sun is a symbol for the highest spiritual Being in many religions.

Force Flow 1 and 4 disappear at the major and minor periods due to the gravitational effect at these times between the sun, moon and earth which causes the forces to cancel out each other. These flows are connected with our Vivaxis which could be called our earth connection, and it is logical that when these earth flows disappear, we can more easily connect with our spiritual source. The receptors on the body associated with the vertical frequency of chromium and the other frequencies on Force Flow 2 remain active at all times. Our connection with Force Flow 3, the magnetic layer, also remains at all times.

Force Flow 3 was called by Fran the magnetic layer. It contains frequencies for iron, sodium, gold, copper, silver and selenium and all these elements in their material form can be used to transport an electrical current. Fran called this layer magnetic because she found it connected with magnetic north and south. The saltwater ice of the North Pole and freshwater ice of the South Pole can be considered in this magnetic sense. Some of Fran's first experiments involved researching the energy flows associated with ice made from fresh and salt water. Force Flow 3 is also associated with negative ions and can be used for increasing this flow of ions in the body. This force flow is 2.54 cm (1 inch) deep.

Force Flow 4 is the same depth and contains frequencies of iodine, zinc and lithium. It is the second flow which disappears at the high and low tides. As these flows are associated with the sun

(Force Flow 1) and the moon (Force Flow 4), we also call them the sun and moon flows. Like the elements associated with Force Flow 1, the Force Flow 4 elements cannot be recorded on the body during high and low tides. Force Flow 4 is associated with positive ions.

The next layer is the phosphorus carrier layer which makes a pair with that of magnesium and is the same size. Like the magnesium carrier band it carries other vibrations and frequencies apart from its main mineral and together with Force Flow 4 is associated with positive ions. The foot band is below the phosphorus band. It has a section for each toe and is the same depth as the hand band. Finally we have the lower white layer which like the upper white layer is associated with the pineal gland. The white layers will be discussed in a later chapter.

In addition to the elements mentioned, the research chemist working with Fran discovered that in between each force flow are frequencies of selenium and germanium which appear to act as one-way switches for energy flow. These two elements are used in modern electronics for a similar purpose. Selenium was found to be involved with the currents or energies moving up through the layers and germanium with the energies moving downwards.

We can enhance our health and well-being by finding and using these earth energies on a regular basis. The energy flows need to be located in a convenient place and marked so that we can use them for channelling and other exercises.

FINDING THE LAYERS AND FORCE FLOWS

As a preliminary measure, make sure your clothes are not synthetic and especially check that your shoes are leather or rubber. Working in bare feet is ideal. Do not wear a hat or spectacles while attempting to locate the layers as they create distortions in the recording process. As with all testing, watches, coins, necklaces and bracelets should be removed. Small earrings are usually not a problem.

1 Choose a time during the solunar flow, that is, in-between high and low tide. Also check for normal ion flow in the environment.

2 Face a gentle slope where the bands will be wide enough to exercise on. The steeper the slope, the narrower the band, and it is difficult to stand straight during the channelling exercises if the ground is too steep (see Diagram 14).

3 Check for neutral ground by placing your left hand face down towards the ground at the level of the heart. If there is no movement in the right or recording hand you are on neutral ground. Neutral ground means that there are no particular force flows whether from the energy layers, underground water, electrical conduits or other sources. Standing on any of these flows interferes with the accurate finding of other flows because we are already then conditioned by that layer on which we stand.

4 Locate Force Flow 1 by humming a tune with eyes shut and gradually tilting your head from front to back while facing the slope. The singing stimulates the horizontal chromium receptors on your head and these are connected to the next chromium horizontal flow above you on the slope. One hand will be found to swing back and forth as you hum and when the centre point of the brain is in alignment with Force Flow 1 both hands will swing. Keep your head still at this point and open your eyes without moving your head to note the position on the ground of Force Flow 1 (see Diagram 15).

To find the exact position of chromium, keep your eyes open and visualise chromium at the position previously noted while humming. Mark this spot with a golf tee or stick. You can further cross-check this flow by visualising one of the other elements on this band such as carbon or calcium and noting a positive response in the recording hand. It is wise to vary the frequencies you

Diagram 15

FINDING THE ENERGY LAYERS

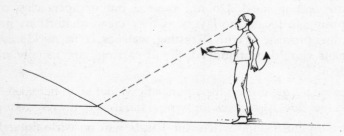

One hand will record energy flow when you stimulate your receptors by humming a tune. When your pineal gland is in line with Force Flow 1 (chromium horizontal) both hands will record a back and forth motion.

visualise so as not to over-saturate your system with any one frequency by concentrating on it for too long.

5 Turn ten degrees to right or left and repeat the procedure. This is to ensure you are not facing in the direction of your Vivaxis or its four quadrants while marking the position of chromium. You will always register a positive response to chromium, calcium and carbon when facing your Vivaxis and thus can get a false direction for the position of the energy layer. If you have correctly located the chromium flow, you will also get a positive response at ten degrees to the left and right of your original direction.

6 Having marked the top of Force Flow 1, scan down the slope visualising chromium and mark the spot where the arm stops recording as this will be the end of this force flow or band. Note that on a gentle slope this band will be much wider than when marking it on a vertical surface where it is only 0.64 cm (0.25 inches) deep. By selecting a gentle slope you can extend this width to up to 30 cm (12 inches) for the purposes of exercising.

7 The end of Force Flow 1 marks the boundary or beginning of Force Flow 2 which is the vertical flow of chromium. The recording hand must be held in the vertical position with fingers curled up pointing towards the sky. Keep visualising chromium and mark where this force flow ends as before. This is the only vertical flow charted on the layers.

8 The next flow to mark is Force Flow 3 by visualising iron or copper while moving your eyes down the slope. This flow will be four times as wide as the previous one. Proceed to mark in all the layers below and above Force Flow 1 by using Diagram 12 as the guide to the elements, their placement and width.

Do not mark the white layers as these are covered in a later chapter after the discussion on the endocrine glands and their connection with the energy flows.

ALTERNATIVE METHOD FOR FINDING APPROXIMATE POSITION OF FORCE FLOW 1

For people who have difficulty using their eyes and who are perhaps more tactile or kinesthetic, I devised an alternative system for finding the energy layers. You still need to visualise chromium but while visualising you sense it through your feet rather than constantly scanning with your eyes. The latter can be tiring especially if you are preparing ten series of practice bands for a seminar as I have on many occasions. Of course this method can also be used to cross-check the first system.

It is especially important in this procedure that if you wear shoes for this exercise they have leather or rubber soles so that the energy flows can be correctly and accurately sensed. You also need to be able to balance easily on one leg when marking the borders of each band!

1 Follow steps one to three as above then hold the recording hand in the position for recording vertical flows and visualise chromium. At the same time find a chromium group with your testing finger on the centre of your forehead. This will help you connect with the Force Flow 2 layer further up the slope from where you are standing. It could be a distance of several yards or metres up this slope. The vertical distance will be indicated by the number of circular swings of the hand while visualising chromium (see Diagram 16). Although you will be finding Force Flow 2 rather than Force Flow 1 as in the previous exercise, the two chromium flows are very close together.

   Your hand will swing a number of swings one way and then the direction will be reversed. Each swing represents about 28 cm (11 inches) of height above your position towards the chromium layer. For instance, if the next band is about 110 cm (44 inches) above your head your recording hand will swing four times one way and four times the other. This motion of the hand continues with a reduced number of swings as we move further up the slope towards the chromium layers.

2 Walk up the slope until your hand stops circulating which happens when you reach the chromium layer.

Diagram 16

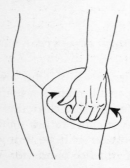

**COUNTING HAND SPINS TO THE
NEAREST CHROMIUM FORCE FLOW**

Your hand will proscribe a number of circles first one way and then the other. The number of circles diminishes as you approach the nearest chromium force flow.

3 Mark this chromium level and having found this approximate position go back down the slope and cross-check the top of Force Flow 1 and 2 by undertaking steps 4–5 of the first method. This is a valuable way to cross-check the finding of Force Flow 1. Then you can stand back on the slope and continue to mark the bands through the feet.

4 When you have marked the top of Force Flow 1, stand facing across the slope with the edge of your left foot against the top of the horizontal chromium band. Visualise chromium, calcium or carbon and record these flows with your recording hand. To cross-check, visualise another element further down the band such as zinc, and the recording arm should stop. In other words, we are recording whatever is under our feet. Lift up your foot and test whether chromium horizontal is still coming through the lower piece of ground under your right foot. Move this foot further down the slope and test whether it is now on the chromium vertical area by holding your hand in the vertical position with fingers curled upwards.

5 Move down the slope visualising elements in each layer and mark the ground as you go at each level. The foot can be moved inch by inch to find the exact edge of the band. Once you become proficient at this method it can be done quite quickly by standing first on one foot and then the other, as you proceed downwards with your feet always placed sideways to the slope.

   The reason you need to lift one foot while testing is so you do not cover too much ground at once. For instance, you may have one foot over Force Flow 2 and the other foot over Force Flow 3 and it would not be possible to know exactly where to mark each band as you would be recording elements from two bands at the same time through your feet.

6 Mark the foot band and then the magnesium band above the chromium band using the same method but Fran advised against actually standing on the hand band. To mark the hand band, stand off the force flows on neutral ground and mark it as for method one. Visualise the hand on the area above the magnesium flow and note the area on the ground where the response in the recording hand ends.

Testing the Force Flows

Now we will begin to discover how to use these energy bands. If you are working with a second person it is valuable to have them check the positions you have marked for all the force flows. Our aim now is to test the energy flow of various articles and if necessary restore them to a balanced state. Recall that healthy energy is recorded as an ion flow whether we are testing animate or inanimate things in our environment. Start to select some articles which do not have a normal ion flow. We can use the energy layers of the earth to restore a normal ion flow in the following manner.

Find a plastic or nylon article and test it for ion flow. A plastic toy would be a good article to test but any article will do. Test this article for ion flow while standing well away from the bands on neutral ground. The recording hand will usually turn in a circular motion indicating a confusion of energies in the plastic object. We can use any of the force flows for re-energising objects but I usually choose Force Flow 1 because of its connection with oxygen. Ideally, if time permits, we should place the articles to be treated on all the force flows for about one minute so that they are subjected to the full range of health-giving frequencies.

So place the article on Force Flow 1 and stand back. Re-test the article on neutral ground after about 20 seconds. The recording arm should now record a back and forth movement indicating a normal and healthy energy flow. You can inactivate all nylon underwear and other synthetic articles from disturbing energies in this fashion. After fifteen years of these experiments, I can still hardly believe my eyes at the permanent changes which appear in synthetic materials using these energies.

The one synthetic plastic which cannot be improved by using the energy bands is acrylic. There must be something in its molecular structure which strongly resists energy flow. This is probably why it can be used to prevent ionising radiation from coming out of television and computer screens. However, acrylic also screens out the healthy energies from the earth when we use it in clothes. Many clothes and shoes are now made of acrylic and this presents a problem in terms of disrupting normal energy flow between the earth and our bodies when we wear this material. You can select an acrylic jumper and test this finding.

Devise your own small research programme. Collect a number of plastic and nylon articles. Treat half of them on the force flows and leave the others. Secretly mark those which are treated. Ask a group of fellow students to test which objects are treated by checking for ion flow. I have carried out such experiments at many seminars and have found a high degree of correlation between the findings of those participants who could accurately test for ion flow.

Exercising on the Energy Layers

The energy layers can now be used for removing static from your body which will prepare you for the next task of finding your Vivaxis. Starting at the magnesium level, exercise on each layer for about two minutes. Keep your feet firmly on the ground; twist and turn in various directions while firmly jarring the body with the heel of the hand. The jarring is to knock out old areas of static so that the force flows may move through these blocked areas. Pay special attention to any areas which have been injured or X-rayed. Finish the exercise on the foot band.

You can saturate your body with an excess of energies during this procedure so it is wise to complete the exercise by moving off the band and grounding your hands on neutral ground for ten seconds. You are now in the correct energy state to find your Vivaxis, but to complete your understanding of the energy flows we need to briefly discuss vertical flows. Fran discovered these after she had researched the horizontal layers for some time.

To understand the whole situation of energy flows in a three-dimensional way visualise the following. The energy layers throughout the the earth and its atmosphere are like layers of an onion and connecting each layer are vertical flows which could be visualised like threads of cotton connecting the skins of the onion. In addition are vectors or force flows for each element which have compass directions and which probably come into our planet from outer space and which therefore connect us with the larger universe.

THE VERTICAL ENERGY FLOWS

During 1981 Fran spent some time exploring the connections between the horizontal layers. These flows are called the vertical flows for obvious reasons. Refer to Diagram 17 for the shape and distribution of these flows and for the list of elements associated with each. Whereas the horizontal layers are continuous in a horizontal plane, the vertical bands may be considered as thin cords of energy which connect the horizontal bands or flows. This can be verified by visualisation and by recording through the feet as one moves from one vertical flow to another.

The vertical sets are repeated every 14 cm ($5^1/_2$ inches) and they are less stable than the horizontal bands being affected by pollution to some degree. It is useful to include both horizontal and vertical flows when energising water. This is why we use a bottle at least

Diagram 17

VERTICAL CONNECTING BANDS AND THEIR ENERGY FLOWS

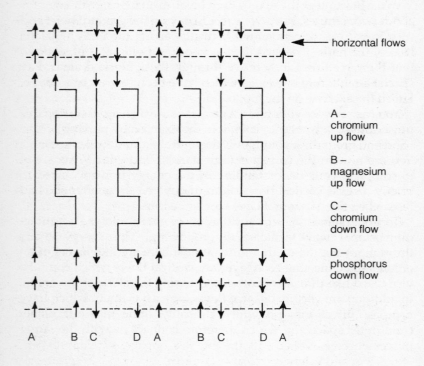

horizontal flows

A –
chromium
up flow

B –
magnesium
up flow

C –
chromium
down flow

D –
phosphorus
down flow

A   B C   D A   B C   D A

The up and down flows are spaced about 14 centimetres
(5¹/₂ inches) apart.

15 cm (6 inches) tall so that when it is rolled on its side it will cross
the vertical flows as well.

Method of Locating the Verticals

Stand on very level ground and move your feet slowly sideways in
an arc. At the same time hold your hand in the recording position
for vertical flows with fingertips pointing upwards, and visualise in
turn magnesium, phosphorus and chromium. When the foot con-
tacts one of the elements the following responses will be noted:

Phosphorus Down Flow – a backward pull on to the heels.
Magnesium Up Flow – a forward or upward pull on to the toes.
Chromium Up Flow – a forward or upward pull on to the toes.
Chromium Down Flow – a backward pull on to the heels.

You will notice from the step shape of the vertical flows in the diagram that a person could mistake the vertical bands for a horizontal one when first looking for the horizontal force flows. This could well explain why beginners sometimes mark the chromium horizontal flow in strange places. The remedy for this error when looking for Force Flow 1 is to scan across the slope to see if horizontal chromium can be found at the same level a short distance to left or right of the first location. Also you should move the feet a few centimetres or inches to left or right for rechecking in case you are standing on a vertical flow for chromium.

One point may need clarification. You would have noted that in the horizontal layer called Force Flow 2 which includes helium and hydrogen that we have chromium but in a vertical wave. I can only assume that this may be the expression of some type of locking mechanism between the horizontal and the vertical flows. It is interesting that the chromium vertical flow is never interrupted by the movements of sun, moon and earth.

FINDING COMPASS DIRECTIONS FOR THE ELEMENTS

So far we have worked with the compass directions for the elements of carbon and calcium (chapter 1). However all the elements have their compass directions. Perhaps we can envisage the energy layers on the earth as being the grounding plates for the elemental frequencies as they travel through space. As this type of research is in its infancy, we have not established whether the directions are similar for all places on earth.

Gradually over the years, individuals working with these force flows have compiled a table of the directions of all the elements. Members of the Vivaxis Energies Research International Society based in Vancouver, Canada have played a big part in this evaluation of directions. Diagram 18 is largely based on their findings. The compass directions on this chart should be compared with other locations but, generally, I have found the elements in the Southern Hemisphere to be in the same compass directions.

For the purpose of charting directions, you can use the same technique that is used for visualising carbon as described in

Diagram 18

DEGREES FROM TRUE NORTH FOR KEY ELEMENTS

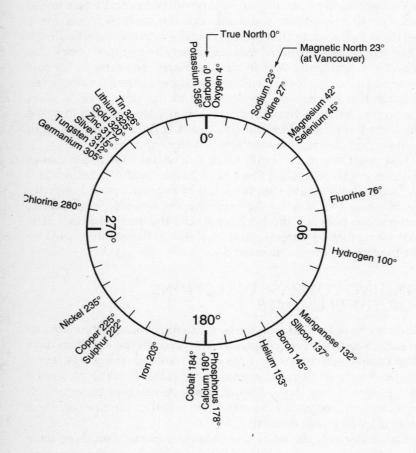

chapter 1. Stand off the energy band on neutral ground and visualise the element concerned during a solunar flow period. One arm should move towards the direction of the element. We then face this direction and ground the hands firmly on the thighs while continuing to visualise the element. Our whole body should then be pulled in the direction of the element. Keep a compass nearby to record the result but place it well away from the area of testing. Like

magnets, a compass will totally distort our evaluations but it is obviously needed to give a reading in degrees measured from magnetic north for each element.

For research purposes, it is a good idea to have several people check the directions of the elements without reference to each other and then to cross-check later. It is also useful to do these experiments at different times and on different days so that the most consistent or basic direction for each element is found.

5

THE VIVAXIS CONNECTION

★ ★ ★ ★ ★ ★

*T*HE electrical pattern is now beginning
to unfold. We are indeed electrical beings with an energy field
associated with a physical body containing thousands of energy
receptors. Each receptor is like a tiny transformer able to receive the
subtle currents which flow if the right mineral frequencies are
present in the receptor and correctly tuned to our Vivaxis.

DISCOVERY OF THE VIVAXIS PHENOMENON

People are always fascinated when I tell the story of how Fran came
to discover what she named the Vivaxis. We have discussed the fact
that the earth is a living body with an energy field interpenetrating
every kingdom in nature. The etheric and electromagnetic field of
the planet therefore conditions our energies as human beings. We
have also explored the idea that each individual has an energy or
etheric body which interfaces with the physical body via an
electromagnetic field and this field can be measured to some degree
by physical instruments. It seems logical therefore that there may be
a connection between our energy field and that of the earth.

Fran Nixon and her husband retired to a beautiful spot just off
Vancouver Island called Thetis Island. They needed a water supply
for their home and Fran taught herself to dowse for water using

metal rods. She became quite expert at this skill and found water for a number of people on the island. One day she decided to experiment with the dowsing rods while holding different substances in her hand.

After some experimentation with inanimate objects she picked some leaves off a tree and was surprised to find that the rod swung in the direction of the tree. It appeared to her that there was an energy flow between the leaf held in her hand and the parent tree or position of the tree. She wondered if people had an energy connection with some point of origin. She experimented with many people and trained them to find the energy flow connecting them to the earth. She called this bundle of energy where our energies connect with those of the earth, the Vivaxis.

In describing how she found her own Vivaxis, Fran originally used two bathroom chains of the type used to secure bath plugs. She woke one morning with the strong impression that we must learn to harness our own energies for healing. Standing erect and with feet apart she turned slowly clockwise a few degrees at a time and noted the movement in the chains held in each hand. At the point where she faced her birthplace, Vancouver, the chains swung strongly back and forth in an alternating movement. The same movement took place when she faced in the opposite direction, and then when she stood at right angles to her birthplace to this position, the chains swung in unison.

Fran described our Vivaxis as an energy duplicate of ourselves which records all the energy changes which take place in our physical bodies and emotions. She saw it as being involved with energy exchange and as a reservoir and receiving station for energies pulsating from the elements deep within the earth, as well as from influences above the earth.

With further investigation Fran concluded that this energy bundle was established at a particular location during the last two months of our mother's pregnancy. Thus the Vivaxis is not necessarily in the home of the mother, but may be found at any place she has been during the last two months of pregnancy. It does not change its position even if we travel to the other side of the globe.

The Vivaxis is the name given to the geographical point where a permanent magnetic alignment was introduced into the atomic structure of our bones as they solidified before birth. Near the time of birth, when the bones solidify, the magnetic pattern becomes fixed in the bones and acquires the specific magnetic characteristics of that position on the earth's surface.[1] We can detect a two-way link to our own individual Vivaxis. The energies flow towards us via one hand and foot and away towards the Vivaxis out the other hand and foot.[2]

CREATING A VIVAXIS

The phenomenon of a Vivaxis is not confined to human beings. A number of processes can all cause a permanent two-way link between the object of the experiment and the place of the experiment or event.[3] To test the site of any Vivaxis, hold one hand palm down over the site and use your recording arm to check for horizontal and vertical waves. The horizontal wave associated with a Vivaxis will always give a circular motion in the recording hand.

The following exercises demonstrate how easily a Vivaxis is created.

- Magnetise a bar of steel by stroking it with a magnet. The Vivaxis will be formed at the place of stroking. In this case, the new magnet has two Vivaxes – one at its place of magnetising and the other connected to the Vivaxis of the first magnet at the original site. This is because the energies introduced to the bar of steel are influenced by the energies from the Vivaxis of the original magnet. Perhaps this example is the most significant to illustrate the confusion of energies which can occur to our own energy fields if we expose ourselves to treatment with magnets.
- Test some seeds in a sprouting tray. You'll find they have a fixed vector or direction to their place of sprouting after a few days of watering. They generally retain this Vivaxis after transplanting to another place. This is a simple experiment which anyone can do.
- Create a Vivaxis by drawing two lines. I have found this the most simple yet revealing way of illustrating the point of Vivaxis. On a piece of paper secured in place, draw two lines about 2.5 cm (1 inch) from opposite ends in quick succession, thus forming one line of 5 cm (2 inches). Wait a few seconds for the Vivaxis to form and then move the piece of paper to a lower level. Then test over the Vivaxis site for a horizontal and vertical wave.

A Vivaxis is also created when magnetising a steel bar by placing it in a coiled wire carrying a direct electric current (DC). The diameter of the Vivaxis is determined by the length of the steel bar. During the life of the magnet there is a flow of energy waves containing both a horizontal and vertical direction between the magnet and its position of origin – its Vivaxis. No matter how far away the magnet is placed from this point, you can test a horizontal and vertical wave over the Vivaxis in the usual manner of testing by holding your hand over the Vivaxis. The magnet needs to be below its Vivaxis so that you can test the vertical waves while holding your testing hand over the Vivaxis.

A Vivaxis is created by a lightning strike. This creates a very strong and permanent Vivaxis and the radius of the Vivaxis is proportional to the length of the tree trunk or pole. In chapter 11 the effect of transferring this Vivaxis to another location is described.

From these examples, it can be seen that a Vivaxis is a permanent sphere of energy, the size of which will vary according to the size of the entity concerned, and which has a permanent two-way link to the subject no how matter great the distance from the original location. It has been found that the energies travel vertically until they reach the level of the subject and then they travel horizontally until they reach the subject (see Diagram 1, page 8). Once you have developed the ability to test horizontal and vertical waves it is simple to evaluate these forces associated with a Vivaxis.

Fran discovered that for accurate testing, and for good health, we need to have clear energy circuits to receive these health-giving energies. Many man-made problems can cause static and energy blocks to these circuits. We have already discussed in chapter 1 how to clear our circuits. The basic fact to remember is that our energy body has both magnetic and electrical components. This has been demonstrated by Harold Saxton Burr in his work on the L-fields, and further developed by Robert Becker in his work with bone regeneration. Becker found that information for growth and re-growth of bones is transmitted by electromagnetic fields which are actually outside of the nervous system.

In his book *Electromagnetism and Life*, Becker states that *evidence seems to be quite conclusive that there are steady DC electrical currents flowing outside the neurones proper throughout the body. These are non-ionic in nature and similar to semi-conducting type currents. Peri-neural cells appear to be the most likely site at which the currents are generated and transmitted*. He further states that this phenomenon constitutes a system of transmission of very basic type data.[4]

ELECTROMAGNETIC DISTURBANCES TO OUR VIVAXIS

Becker also did an enormous amount of work on the effect of man-made electromagnetic fields on those of the human body. It appears that our delicate electrical nature is easily overpowered by the fields associated with power lines, television screens, and transformers. Electromagnetic interference of a much higher frequency is encountered from the microwave transmitters which are now all over our globe. Becker researched how the electromagnetic fields from household appliances such as refrigerators, hairdryers, computer terminals, electric blankets and some electrical circuits and cellular phones have all been shown to have detrimental effects on the body.

Since Fran first made her discoveries, our exposure to many of these fields has greatly increased and the last chapter of this book is devoted to exploring this area more fully. At this stage of our study, we need to briefly note these facts about electromagnetic fields and their effect on the Vivaxis energies, in order to understand the need to clear our Vivaxis circuits of foreign energies.

Further assaults to our own circuits of energy include exposure to medical investigations such as X-rays, ultrasounds, CAT scans, nuclear magnetic resonators, and electro-cardiographs. Many chemicals in drugs and foods may also upset our energies. I have found disturbances in a number of people caused by electronic gadgets which some natural therapists use. Electrical circuitry in the machine can create a foreign Vivaxis which then confuses the energy of the person. Sometimes a person is literally in a seething sea of energy and a number of foreign Vivaxes can be detected in their field.

One of my naturopathic clients who had studied Vivaxis with me had some treatment from a practitioner involving a machine which pulsed energies at different frequencies. Several people were hooked up to the machine for each session at a particular frequency. On one day this practitioner would treat cancer patients, the next day asthmatic patients would receive treatment, and at another time people with arthritis would be treated. This situation allowed these people to become permanently linked together (electrically speaking) via the machine. My client came back to me after experiencing sensations like electric shocks in her body and had realised what she had done in terms of her Vivaxis.

On scanning her field, I discovered that she had a foreign field connected to her wrist at the point where the electrode from the machine had been attached during the treatment. She had not informed me of this point of contact before the scanning took place. In her case, after attempting unsuccessfully to eradicate the problem, we had to make her a new personal Vivaxis (see chapter 10).

Methods to Remove Disturbances from our Vivaxis Channel

Over the years, a number of methods have been used for clearing energy blocks from the Vivaxis circuits. They all involve techniques which neutralise or carry away excess electrical energy, particularly in the form of static.[5]

THE WIRE HOOP METHOD

This very simple method requires you to stand in a galvanised wire hoop. The hoop should have one end of the wire pointing into the circle and one end pointing outwards. The circle needs to be one metre (3–4 feet) in diameter. You should stand inside the circle with hands grounded on your thighs, feet placed apart but not touching the wire. You only need to spend thirty seconds inside the circle. The rationale here is obvious – the inside end in the circle picks up excess energy from the person and carries it away. It is preferable to undertake this clearing outside because of the many electrical circuits in your house.

This method is suitable for simple static or excess energy problems. It is an old technique which has been used in many ways. For instance, a wire or strap was often attached to a car so that it dragged along the road and presumably discharged static which had accmulated during travel. This was supposed to prevent car sickness.

THE SODA AND SALT BATH

Take a half kilogram or sixteen ounces of sodium bicarbonate and the same amount of unrefined sea salt and add it to a bath of water. You must soak in the bath for about ten minutes and immerse your head a few times. Again, this method is mainly suitable for general static and works best with pure water which is not available in most cities today. The many chemicals in our water supply may interfere with the exchange of energy between the soda, salt and the body. This procedure should not be undertaken for three days over the full moon period because they energy transmitted by these compounds is temporarily unstable.

HOT SHOWER SPRAY

This is a means whereby you are stimulated by the negative ions which are present in running water. The negative ions tend to remove static and energise the body. Your head must be immersed and the water must be allowed to go inside your mouth to stimulate tongue, teeth and surrounding area. Again, the many impurities in water today may detract from the effectiveness of this method. If we get caught in a rainstorm we are also bombarded by negative ions and this may account for a feeling of being energised (provided it is not freezing weather).

EXERCISING ON THE ENERGY LAYERS

Exercising on these layers (see page 65) is the most successful method we have found for removing energy blocks, and for re-energising the body with all the frequencies needed for a healthy life. Remember to exercise on each of the force flows with your feet firmly on the ground, your closed fists jarring each part of your body, while you twist and turn your body in different directions. The twisting action is important because each life-giving element is connected to a particular direction in space.

Exercising in this manner on the energy layers allows us to pick up frequencies through our feet from the layer on which we stand and as we face various directions with the twisting movements we also receive frequencies from different compass directions. The exact compass direction for each element is in Diagram 18. Although these are the main directions, the elements are also found to come in to some extent from other directions depending on the position of the earth at a particular time of day.

About two minutes of exercising on each of the central six energy flows is sufficient after you have cleared your body with carbon. Carbon clearing is far more effective if it is done while facing west and standing on the layer which contains the frequency of carbon. As described in chapter 1, if you are not standing on the energy layers, carbon is located by facing north and not west. Somehow the direction of carbon is changed as the energy flows through the energy layers of the earth.

The neutralising exercise is another instance where there is an enhancement to the procedure by sitting on Force Flow 1.

THE HUMAN ENERGY FIELD

Before I describe how to find your Vivaxis, we need to discuss the human energy field in a bit more detail. In classical Trans-Himalayan teaching, there are seven layers of consciousness and seven vehicles for this consciousness. We touched on these levels of consciousness in the first two chapters. The physical body is only the outer coat and the first vehicle of significance is understood to be the energy field which underlies all physical organs and tissues. In the West this energy body is often termed the etheric body. The purpose of this energy body is threefold:

- To provide the pattern for all physical growth and regrowth – the blueprint described by Burr in his research on the L-fields.

- To receive energy from the sun and to transport it to every part of the physical body.

- To act as a mediator between the higher states of consciousness and the brain and nervous system.[6]

The physical interface between the etheric body and the physical appears to be an electromagnetic field. Becker clearly established that information for growth and regrowth within the body is transmitted by this field. His research explains what is presently inexplicable in embryology, that is, why does an ear grow on the head and not on the toe! It is the etheric body which provides the blueprint or pattern which is then transmitted by the electromagnetic field to the cells. The scientific basis for the etheric body has been explored in a previous book of mine entitled *Frontiers of Natural Therapy*.[7]

Kirlian photography highlights the electromagnetic field of the human body and how it changes before observable disease takes place. The object or subject to be photographed is placed in a high frequency field which causes an acceleration of electrons to be given off from the skin. These electrons then collide with molecules in the air which create light that manifests as an aura on the film without any external light source being necessary for the photo. The scientific name for this effect is coronal discharge.

It is understandable therefore that the etheric vehicle is often called the light body. We now know that excited electrons can become light particles or photons which have movement but no mass. The human body has been found to emit light particles all the time and a number of electronic scientists attracted to the leading edge of medicine have been researching how to record this light body.

One of the leaders in the field is Harry Oldfield in the United Kingdom. He has designed a video camera and software programme which captures the light body on a computer screen, thus allowing coloured prints to be made without the need for a high frequency field. Blocks of colour on the images received are interpreted as blockages of energy and have been found to coincide with physical problems in the subject. To date there is no detailed published material on his technology or research but some background reading to his work is featured in his book *The Dark Side of the Brain*.[8]

We always need to be careful to distinguish the electromagnetic field around the body from the etheric body which is probably beyond the range of the electromagnetic spectrum. However, the etheric body appears to interpenetrate and express itself through the electromagnetic field, and thus high frequency photography and the more refined technique of Oldfield may give us indirect but important information about the etheric energies of a person.

From Fran's research, the etheric body appears to have a band of two layers outside the skin and this was described in the previous chapter as being associated with the frequency of two particular groups of elements essential for life. Healthy people have a free two-way energy flow back and forth from this envelope around the body to the Vivaxis. We considered earlier the interference from man-made technology on this electrical envelope of energies around our body. This detrimental effect occurs because in the human body we are dealing with milli-volts and a very weak electromagnetic field compared with the much stronger electromagnetic fields associated with modern technology.

It is not surprising that Fran found the Vivaxis connection disturbed in many people. Medical researchers have now established a close link between the nervous and immune systems. As there is also a link between the electromagnetic field of the human and the nervous system, it is understandable that the immune system could be severely compromised by electromagnetic interference.

FINDING YOUR VIVAXIS

When Fran first began to teach people to find their Vivaxis she used two galvanised angle wires which were bent in a right angle with the vertical arm held in a copper sleeve. The person looking for their Vivaxis turned around slowly in a circle and when they were in their Vivaxis channel the wires crossed neatly at the tips. Alternatively, they used one wire which swung towards the tip of the index finger of the other hand when facing the Vivaxis. The body position was important; the spine was held quite straight, head erect, and the wires were held out in front of the body with the copper sleeve in a vertical position and the thumb in a vertical position on the copper sleeve.[9]

For research purposes, I still sometimes play with a pair of angle wires, usually copper, and even without a sleeve covering one arm of the wire, I can make interesting observations. For testing the body energies or dowsing of any kind, the wires must be held with the horizontal portion of the wire parallel to the ground. The wire must be able to turn freely above the first finger and thumb which is holding the vertical arm of the wire. I have found that if you are free from energy disturbances, and concentrate strongly on a particular direction, one wire will turn strongly towards the Vivaxis and the other in the direction dictated by the brain.

As the years went by Fran discovered more and more about the elements and their frequencies. She noticed that impurities such as lead frequencies in the wire were absorbed into the body, and affected the recording ability of the students. It was at this stage that she started to train people to use their arm as the recording instrument instead of using a rod or pendulum. I am in agreement with these findings having initially experimented with the wires I now find it more natural to use my arm and hand.

There are several techniques which can be used for finding your Vivaxis. Clearing your circuits is essential before attempting to locate your Vivaxis. You should do the carbon clearing for X-rays, the neutralising exercise and exercising on the energy flows before undertaking the next step. Also be aware that if you have blocked sinuses you may not be able to find your Vivaxis until this trouble is resolved. This is probably because your magnetic sense is located near the ethnoid sinus, close to the root of the nose and may be disturbed with sinusitis.

As an interesting prelude to this exercise, scan each side of your hand for the Vivaxis flows. From the previous exercises with the triple groups you are used to finding iron and zinc or iodine in these groups. There will be a flow of the magnetic group including iron down one side of the hand and down the other side the flow will include iodine or zinc as the main element of the gravitational group.[10] (see Diagram 19).

You will remember that these correspond to the same mineral groups from the energy layers of the earth and our Vivaxis connects us with these energy flows. Visualise the element iron while scanning one edge of your hand and if there is no response in your recording hand then think of your element in the gravitational group which you have already established as zinc or iodine. Once you have become skilled at linking up with the Vivaxis you will find that as soon as you pick up any of the Vivaxis flows in your

Diagram 19

VIVAXIS FLOWS ALONG THE SIDES OF THE HANDS

The magnetic flow will be on one side of your hand and the gravitational flow on the other. This forms part of the two-way flow back and forth to your Vivaxis.

body, your recording arm will move in the direction of your Vivaxis while you concentrate on that element. However, in the meantime, the following methods will help you to find the exact direction for the flows connected with your Vivaxis.

METHOD 1

1 Test for neutral ground and find an area at least 2 metres (7 feet) away from buildings and trees and at least 18 metres (50 feet) away from street power lines, and be clear by some 2 metres (6 feet) of the electric line leading to your house.

2 Test for ion flow on yourself and include your environment by turning clockwise. Never do any exercises if your hand records a circular motion which indicates chaotic energies in self or environment.

3 Test for solunar flow because during the high and low tides the Vivaxis link is not fully present.

4 Find the energy layers and stand on Force Flow 3 (magnetic band). Rest the three middle fingers of one hand on the side of the thigh at the place where they naturally touch; a triple group is located here. The recording hand should now move as for ion flow. The three fingers will be matching their same groups on the thigh – iron, chromium and zinc or iodine – and when you lift the middle finger your other fingers will remain connected to the Vivaxis flows of the magnetic and gravitational groups (see Diagram 20).

5 After you have lifted the middle finger, your recording hand and arm should now turn and start swinging towards the Vivaxis

Diagram 20

FINDING THE TRIPLE GROUPS ON THE THIGHS

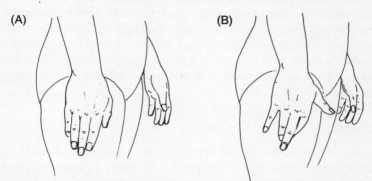

(A)   (B)

When your three fingers are correctly placed on the side of the thigh (A)
your recording arm will move back and forth (same as ion flow). Lift the
middle finger which leaves the two Vivaxis fingers on the Vivaxis groups
(B) and your recording arm should now move in the direction of your
Vivaxis. After turning to face your Vivaxis, both arms should swing back
and forth towards your Vivaxis.

following the energies related to the Vivaxis fingers. Try turning in different directions because in some positions the body
may be in the way of the arm swinging towards your Vivaxis.
Facing different directions will also reconfirm the direction of the
Vivaxis.

6 Mark the position with a stick and turn your feet so that you are
directly facing towards your Vivaxis. Ground your hands firmly
on your thighs and hum a tune learnt early in life such as a
nursery rhyme. The reason for singing a nursery rhyme is
because this melody was firmly in your memory bars at an age
before any disturbances to your Vivaxis occurred. Hence reviving
an early childhood musical memory causes a strong pull towards
your Vivaxis and your whole body will probably be pulled
forward towards this point.

Note that when you stand on Force Flow 3 and face your Vivaxis
you will be pulled forward when you visualise any of the elements
on the force flow such as iron, copper or selenium. For this reason
when testing compass directions for the elements as described in
the previous chapter, it is important not to be facing any of your
Vivaxis quadrants because when facing your Vivaxis, its opposite

direction or at right angles, you will obtain a pull when visualising any of the elements.

If ever you are pushed backwards when facing your Vivaxis it is possible there is a thunderstorm or some other disturbing influence in the Vixaxis area, and testing and channelling should be postponed until the influence disappears. However, in the early stages it is wise to check that you are not standing with your back to the Vivaxis. Check by reversing directions and humming a nursery rhyme again.

METHOD 2

1 Stand on Force Flow 3 and repeat Steps 1–3 of Method 1. Then place the middle finger of your left hand lightly on your navel.

2 Turn slowly anti-clockwise if you are in the Southern Hemisphere and clockwise if in the Northern Hemisphere. When you face your Vivaxis your recording arm will swing as it does for ion flow. This is the only position where you will get a recording of ion flow from the navel. It is almost as if we have an invisible umbilical cord of energy attaching us to the Vivaxis.

You can use this method to cross-check the first method. It may happen that with this technique you also get a response when facing the exact opposite direction of your Vivaxis. In this case use the humming of the nursery rhyme to distinguish between the two directions. We are usually only pulled forward when facing the Vivaxis.

Once we have cleared our energy circuits of X-rays, and other disturbances, we should be able to stand facing any direction in a relaxed state with a quiet mind and one arm should swing in the direction of our Vivaxis. To make sure that your X-rays have been removed, press your middle finger firmly on the parts which have been X-rayed and the recording arm should still swing towards your Vivaxis. If it moves in another direction, this means that you are receiving energy from two Vivaxes, your own and one connected with an X-ray machine or some other electromagnetic source.

You must then repeat the carbon technique for X-rays, repeat the neutralising exercise, jar the area concerned again, and exercise on all the force flows again, concluding by channelling to the Vivaxis as described in the next chapter.

Testing the Strength of the Vivaxis Energies

The Vivaxis can also be found when you stand on neutral ground. However, when a person is facing their Vivaxis on ordinary ground they drain the energies of anything in their environment within a radius of 60 metres (200 feet). This indicates the amazing energies of our Vivaxis and can be demonstrated.

Arrange to have several people who are proficient at finding ion flow at various distances up to about 60 metres (200 feet) from a person (A) standing on neutral ground. Have these testers find ion flow and then re-test when the person (A) is facing their Vivaxis. The testers' recording arms will go completely dead when anyone faces their Vivaxis, illustrating the strength of the energies with which we are dealing. This test should not be done for more than a minute as it is obviously draining energy from everyone in the vicinity.

These results also indicate the amazing protective effect of the energy layers and for this reason all Vivaxis work should be done on these bands to protect and strengthen our energy field, and to protect other people. Of all the therapies I have studied in natural medicine involving subtle energies, my work with earth energies does provide repeatability. This suggests to me that we are dealing with a science.

THE SIGNIFICANCE OF THE VIVAXIS

It is an impressive finding that all creatures have magnetic waves which link directly to a geographic point established shortly before birth. These waves supply life-giving forces in a two-way magnetic link. It is also significant that a lay person established that we have a magnetic faculty to find this direction long before scientists found that humans, animals, fish and birds have this magnetic or homing sense of direction.

The fact that our energy field is connected through a bundle of energy to the energy field of the earth is a logical and yet extraordinary finding. It means that we are truly children of mother Earth. If we destroy our Vivaxis, another one is made immediately which is connected to the nearest energy layer (see chapter 10). We can speculate that in some cases of unexplained death, for some reason, a person's Vivaxis is destroyed and no new connection made. One wonders what effect extra-planetary travel has on astronauts with respect to their Vivaxis.

The sphere of energy which is the Vivaxis does not disappear even after death. Of course there will no longer be the two-way link connecting it with the animal or human in the absence of a physical or etheric body. This is a hard subject to research on a large scale because we would have to know the exact place of each person's Vivaxis to test whether it remains after death. According to the writings of Fran Nixon we only have limited cases where the actual location of the pre-natal Vivaxis has been found.

For maintaining health and connecting with our Vivaxis it is not necessary to find its place of origin. What we do need to find is the exact direction of the Vivaxis. In theory, we could find the place by following this direction to its source through continual checking and testing on route.

Even if you lived only a few miles from the place of residence of your mother during pregnancy, this would be quite a challenge on foot. You could do it by car but this would be very difficult to perform accurately on any road which is close to power lines. Also, the effect on your energies while travelling in the car would tend to cause inaccurate recording until you had grounded yourself again by walking around for a while. This is a point to remember when doing any of these techniques after travelling by car, train or plane.

However, a number of people in country areas who have not moved far from their birthplace have been able to find their Vivaxis, and this has provided valuable information. For general purposes, it is quite unnecessary to find the actual place of the Vivaxis. We soon learn to test whether there is a clear channel. In this day of technology, despite electric cables, wires, microwave transmitters and machines which our Vivaxis flows must traverse, in most cases, the energies stay intact. So let us now explore how we can use these amazing energies for improving our health.

6
USING THE VIVAXIS AND ENERGY LAYERS

★ ★ ★ ★ ★ ★

O VER the years I have learnt many practical ways to use these earth energies to restore health to ourselves and the environment. The great advantage of this work with earth energies is that it costs nothing and can be done by each individual for themselves. It is especially useful after travelling, during stress, illness or at any time when we are thrown completely back on our own resources.

Channelling the Vivaxis energies is the most significant exercise we can do in relation to our Vivaxis. It is a means of consolidating our life-giving Vivaxis energies and restoring these energies to disturbed parts. By channelling, the individual brings the energies of the entire body into phase through currents which run in parallel flows to and from the Vivaxis. The alignment of all the elements in the body is strengthened which in turn corrects nervous and muscular abnormalities. There is also a dramatic effect on the lymphatic system and immune function. This means that foreign viruses and bacteria can be overcome. In addition, all the endocrine glands are aligned and balanced.

The following factors need to be observed and avoided during channelling as they can interfere with our Vivaxis energies: aeroplanes passing overhead, nearby electric motors such as chainsaws or power-drills, garden mowers, thundery weather conditions, tree branches overhead, nearby power lines, standing on acrylic carpet or directly under lights or near television or FM transmitters. Select an open space outside during calm weather away from these interferences.

You need not channel every day; the need will vary and perhaps twice a week may be a rough guide for maintaining or restoring health. To guide myself in this respect, I walk slowly across the energy layers and observe whether I get a response in my recording arm on any force flow. If so, I use that as an indication to channel on that force flow. It is usually Force Flow 1, 3 or 4. Occasionally, for a specific purpose such as the need for more negative or positive ions, it is appropriate to channel on the magnesium or phosphorus band.

Check the following key areas for healthy ion flow: top of the head, coccyx, centre points in the hands and feet, and the back of the hard palate. Use the tip of your thumb to test the palate. If a disturbance is found, jar the areas before channelling.

CHANNELLING TO THE VIVAXIS

1 Remove watches, jewellery, hats and shoes unless they have rubber or leather soles.

2 Check ion and solunar flows. Never channel during high or low tides, or at new or full moon for at least four hours before and after. The exact times of full and new moons are given on many calendars. Be careful to adjust for summer times as calendars do not include these times. If it is summer time, you will need to subtract one hour from clock time to revert to real time.

3 Find the best force flow to use by slowly walking over the band from the foot band to magnesium until your recording arm gives a strong response. If in doubt, use Force Flow 1 or 3.

4 Stand on the chosen flow and find the direction of your Vivaxis. The four quadrants can then be marked exactly on the ground – each direction will be exactly ninety degrees from the next. Now channel in the four directions in the following manner starting and finishing by facing your Vivaxis. Stand with feet apart, spine erect, shut your eyes and tilt your head as far forward as possible. Gradually raise your head and move it as far backwards as possible. Note the response in your arms. If your arms respond very strongly at any point keep your head at that tilt and wait until your arms have stopped moving which indicates that sufficient energy has been absorbed (see Diagram 21).

Diagram 21

CHANNELLING TO THE VIVAXIS

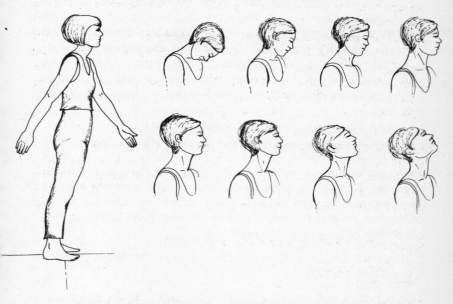

Your arms swing back and forth as you channel to your Vivaxis.
Gradually tilt your head as shown.

5 Turn anti-clockwise for the Southern Hemisphere and reverse for the Northern Hemisphere and repeat in the four directions, finishing by channelling a fifth time when you are facing your Vivaxis again.

6 Exercise briefly on the other force flows except on the hand band.

7 Move off the bands and ground your hands on neutral ground to remove excess energy.

8 Test if the process has been effective by observing whether your arm will only move towards the Vivaxis even when concentrating on another direction. This indicates that the body is still strongly aligned to the Vivaxis.

9 Walk around for twenty minutes or so to ground your energies and stay away from other people while your body fluids are strongly aligned to your Vivaxis. The fluids in your body remain aligned with your Vivaxis for about twenty minutes after

channelling. This fact can be verified by touching any of your lymph nodes with your testing finger (remember – left index finger if you are higher than your Vivaxis and your left ring finger if you are below). The recording arm will be stimulated to move for twenty minutes. The alignment can be cut short at any time by briefly doing the neutralising exercise using the accordion method described in chapter 1. After twenty minutes has elapsed, or sooner if you have done the neutralising exercise, your arm will move towards any direction which is visualised.

CHANNELLING FOR SPECIFIC ELEMENTS

There are occasions when it is important to channel for specific elements. For instance, channelling to iron in cases of anaemia; selenium to improve immunity; or iodine in cases of thyroid deficiency. At other times we need extra oxygen to counter bad headaches and various infections.

1 Stand on the force flow which contains the chosen element (see Diagram 12).

2 Stand erect and visualise the element and note the direction in which the recording arm moves. Face that direction and ground your hands on your thighs while visualising that element. If you are facing the correct direction, your body should be pulled forward while visualising the element concerned. Mark the ground in four directions at points ninety degrees apart from the first and main direction for that element.

3 Channel in the same way as you do to your Vivaxis, facing the four directions associated with the element.

4 Exercise briefly on the other force flows except the hand band to balance with the other elements.

Remember that channelling must be done during the solunar flow because otherwise the energy flows from elements like chromium, calcium, iodine and zinc will have temporarily disappeared. Channelling for selenium is particularly strong during the low tide and we should always endeavour to channel at that time for selenium if it is needed. As selenium is very important for immunity this can be a most valuable exercise.

METHOD FOR ALLEVIATING THE COMMON COLD

1 Stand on Force Flow 1 and stimulate the sinus receptors on the ends of your toes by shuffling and pressing them on the ground.

2 Wrap ice cubes in plastic and stimulate the sinus receptors on the ends of your fingers by holding the ice on each fingertip for a few seconds. Gently press the cubes around your sinus cavities on sides of your nose and around your eyes and ears.

3 Channel to your Vivaxis as usual and inhale and exhale deeply in each of the four positions. Swallow twice in each direction to flex throat muscles and to direct magnetic energies to the throat.

This procedure may need to be repeated in two hours and for best results it should be used at the first sign of a cold or flu.[1]

HINTS FOR TRAVELLERS

When travelling around it is useful to know the general directions of north, south, east and west because then you will always be aware of the general direction of your Vivaxis. Travelling quickly, or over long distances can tend to skew your perception of your Vivaxis direction and it may appear to be at right angles to its true direction. Therefore it is wise to exercise on the central force flows 1–4, after you have been subject to a disturbance like jet travelling or other electrical or magnetic interferences. I have not found these interferences prevented me from finding the energy layers after travel.

Locate Force Flow 1 after arriving at your destination; you can then proceed to check for the direction of your Vivaxis. Hopefully the direction you find coincides with your rough evaluation of compass directions, and you can proceed to channel on a force flow. If it still appears to be at right angles it is probably necessary to stress (jar) the key points on the skull while exercising further on the force flows. Affected points could be the top of the head, roof of mouth, bridge of nose, and mastoid bone behind the ear.

INACTIVATING OUR ENVIRONMENT

You have already used energy flows to inactivate or treat plastic and nylon articles. Now it is time to extend this activity. It is possible to carry this inactivating influence from the energy flows to other

environments.[2] One of the first exercises I ask seminar participants to undertake is to inactivate the harmful vibrations of modern
buildings and man-made substances used in cars and furniture.

Make an 'inactivator' bag by mixing a heaped tablespoon of
calcium ascorbate with half a kilogram of organic wheat bran. This
mixture is tightly sealed in a strong, clear plastic bag which is
placed on each force flow for half a minute. The vitamin C appears
to absorb all the frequencies of the force flows and to retain them for
years provided it does not become damp. Vitamin C has been
shown by medical scientists to be involved with electron transfer in
the cell and is therefore sensitive to energy transfer. So perhaps this
exercise is not as eccentric as it sounds.

Test the furnishings in your house for ion flow. Use the eyes for
scanning and note the response in the recording hand. Disturbed
furnishings will cause the recording hand to move in a circular
fashion instead of the healthy back and forth motion. Alternatively,
there may be a complete lack of movement. It is interesting to test
different furnishings such as carpets, chairs and beds for ion flow.
Many disturbances will be found except in the case of completely
natural substances like untreated timber, wool, straw and cotton.
All painted surfaces will tend to give disturbed recordings as will
wallpapers, synthetic carpets, and floors sealed with polyurethane
compounds.

After testing, swing the bag systematically over all areas starting
at the far side of each room and moving away from areas just
inactivated. Ideally, the process would be undertaken on the roof as
everything below the roof would then be treated. This could certainly be carried out on a flat roof but may be a hazardous exercise
if it is sloping! Allow a few moments for the energies to settle before
re-testing. Your arm should give a healthy back and forth movement after treating the area concerned (see Diagram 22).

The same technique is used for the car. In most cases this can be
done by swinging the bag over the car from outside. Best to
undertake these activities when the neighbours are not watching!
Many people comment on the difference in the atmospheres of
their homes, offices and cars after treatment with the inactivator
bag. The bag should not be stored next to where people sleep or
on any vibrating household items such as washing machines or
refrigerators.

The same technique can be used over food substances to remove
the frequencies of cadmium and lead, or mercury which is often
present in fish. The inactivator does not of course remove the

Diagram 22

INACTIVATING THE HOME

Start on the far side of the room and move backwards
towards the door.

physical molecules of these harmful elements, but what seems to happen is that the harmful vibrations or frequencies corresponding to the element in question disappear permanently.

It is necessary to clarify here the various responses we have in our recording hand. If we are not thinking of anything in particular, normal healthy energy will be recorded as a back and forth movement. The direction of this movement is not important but is usually towards and away from the side of the body. An energy disturbance from a detrimental substance will usually give a circulating movement. However, if you are visualising a particular substance such as lead and it is present you will get a back and forth movement which is literally saying 'yes', lead is present. Our hand therefore responds to our intention – whether testing for normal energy as in ion flow, or whether testing for a particular element which is visualised.

As a research exercise, you could test whether various objects contain harmful substances. For instance, you could look at small bottles of leaded and unleaded petrol and test which contains lead by visualising lead as in lead weights. If lead is present, your recording arm should give a positive or back and forth response when visualising for lead. The responses should then be recorded and some of the samples containing lead should be inactivated by a person not involved with the testing. The samples could then be re-tested and results compared.

You could also test unsprayed fruit and vegetables from bio-dynamic farms and compare it with supermarket produce. There is no end to the small projects which you can do to test the effect of the Vivaxis flows and the energy layers. Your body is a most sensitive instrument for diagnosis. The inactivator material will eventually cease to work and this can be assessed by testing objects before and after inactivating. The material should then preferably be burnt. I have found that it can retain its potency for years.

Earth energies are quite powerful so a few notes of caution are appropriate. Two inactivators should not be stored within a short distance of each other in a house, office or car. This is because lines of force are formed between the two inactivator bags. If a person had to work or sleep in a line between two inactivators, their body energies may be disturbed.

The same energies from the energy layers can be used to deflect harmful but naturally-occurring phenomena such as underground streams, and this will be described later when we look at a number of environmental issues.

ENERGISING WATER

One of the simple ways you can use the energies of the energy bands is by treating water on the energy flows.[3] Each person must establish for themselves how often this is needed. If you have an infection or illness you may need to dose yourself with the treated water more often than normally.

Known as hydrotherapy, the use of energised water was the first organised movement of natural therapies which developed in the nineteenth century. The use of water to cleanse and heal goes back thousands of years to earliest recorded history. Early medical physicians such as Hippocrates and Galen used water to dress wounds.

Water appears to absorb earth energies very readily as has been demonstrated in research associated with homeopathy. After the 30th dilution of one part homeopathic substance to one hundred parts of water there are no physical molecules of the substance left, yet we know from our clinical work that these very high dilutions can have a powerful effect in restoring health. By energising water on the force flows, the resonance of the various elements seems to be imprinted on the water for a considerable time. By drinking the water daily, the molecular balance of the elements in your body can be restored. You can also absorb the health-giving elements more adequately from your food.

Like every form of therapy involving energies, one must take care not to overdose. This is why natural therapies such as homeopathic doses are administered sparingly to avoid confusion, or creation of excess energies. It is best to use the energised water no more than once daily except in cases of acute disorders such as sore throat, inflamed bowel or other acute infections. Even in such cases, only a few mouthfuls of water every couple of hours should be taken.

METHOD FOR ENERGISING WATER TO DRINK

1 Choose a time when environmental conditions are stable and test for balanced ion flow and for solunar flow period.

2 Fill a jar with rainwater or filtered water – a jar which measures at least 15 cm (6 inches) tall so that when placed on its side it will cover the vertical energy bands in addition to the horizontal flows. The material of the lid can be tin or plastic.

3 Roll the jar between the force flows from the magnesium down to and including the phosphorus band. If you need more negative ions finish rolling the jar and drink the water while you stand on the magnesium flow. If you need more positive ions finish rolling the jar and drink the water while standing on the phosphorus layer.

4 Now test the water using visualisation for the essential elements such as calcium, magnesium, zinc, iron, chromium and so on. Your recording arm will move back and forth for as long as you visualise each element, providing the frequency of the element is present in the energised water.

5 Drink about half a cup.

The energised water will retain the frequencies absorbed from the energy bands for about fifteen minutes but will lose its potency fairly quickly after placing the bottle on the ground. Therefore drink it immediately after the rolling procedure. If the water is rolled between 10 a.m. and 2 p.m. to include the white force flows (see chapter 9) then the water retains the frequencies for weeks if placed in a stable location.

The energised water can be used as an inactivator by placing it in a bag and using as described above for inactivating the environment. Never drink water which has been used for inactivating – discard it as soon as you have completed the inactivating. Using water for inactivating food and drink can be very useful if you don't have calcium ascorbate and bran. As the water loses its properties quickly (unless including the white flows) you won't have the problem of conflicting forces which can arise from the ascorbate powder. The latter retains its power for many years and will create a field of energy when near other inactivating material.

The energy frequencies in your own body can be tested by rolling a jar of un-energised water up your body from a few centimetres (2 inches) below the navel to just above the eyebrows. Then place the jar upright on a table and visualise the various elements in the water. If an element is missing, then help yourself absorb that frequency by drinking water which has been energised on the relevant force flows. You should also exercise on that force flow.

Water that is not distilled or filtered may contain various minerals both healthy and otherwise. The only filtering method which removes all foreign substances is the process called reverse osmosis. This process involves passing the water under pressure through a very fine membrane which even removes bacteria. The popular and cheap water purifiers which have carbon filters remove a few substances but not those which are more fully dissolved in the water. Water from an underground source is usually rich in those elements from the surrounding rocks and soil and cannot be used for the above exercises.

HEALING A DISTURBED ROOM USING SALTWATER AND FRESHWATER

Due to atmospheric changes, the sick-building syndrome, earthquakes which affect the energy field of wide areas and other factors, we sometimes need to balance the energies in a room. If the ion flow in a room is severely disturbed it will be difficult for people to concentrate. The easiest way to test for unbalanced ion flow has been described in chapter 2. This exercise illustrates the relation of ion flow to magnetic north and south.

1 Dissolve one teaspoon of real sea salt to half a litre or one pint of purified water and stir with a wooden spoon or shake until dissolved. Pour into a jar and freeze the water.

2 Take a second jar of frozen freshwater. The jars must be at least 30 cm (12 inches) apart and are placed in line between magnetic north and south with the saltwater north of the freshwater. Notice that we are copying the arrangement of the water which is found at the north and south poles – salt in the north and fresh in the south. Remove jars if the atmosphere becomes too saturated with negative ions.

A strong inactivating influence spreads around the jars and up to the ceiling of the room. This technique is useful for reaching pollutants in the ceiling which are hard to access.

STIMULATING AND IMPROVING THE MEMORY

Among the many health concerns which clients discuss with me 'memory' is probably top of the list. It is a grave concern to us all when we start to experience memory lapses. We worry that the brain is no longer a reliable instrument. The fear of some form of senility lurks in the mind of many of us especially as we approach middle-age and observe severe memory lapses in our elderly parents.

There are many vitamin and mineral supplements containing substances such as the B-complex and magnesium and potassium phosphate which can be of great assistance. However, if the basic receptors on the head for these minerals are disturbed, we need to get to the cause. You will remember that in finding your Vivaxis, you used an old memory like a nursery rhyme to verify the direction of your Vivaxis. This was done because the memories of such rhymes were formed before any damage to your receptors had occurred from chemicals, deficiencies, or electromagnetic sources.

In this exercise, we stimulate the key memory receptors which are in a band around your head at the level of the bridge on your nose (see Diagram 33).

1 Check ion and solunar flow.

2 Drink energised water which has been rolled between the magnesium and phosphorus bands.

3 Stand on Force Flow 3 because the elements associated with your memory receptors are in this flow.

4 Find the direction of your Vivaxis.

5 Face your Vivaxis. Find the memory receptor on the bridge of the nose with the tip of your testing finger by visualising in turn

the elements associated with the magnetic group – iron, copper, selenium, and gold. Your recording arm should swing in response to each visualisation. Repeat the process to find the corresponding receptors at the back of the head and those at the side of the head above the ears. These receptors will be in a direct line with those on the nose.

6 Using your index fingers press the receptors on your nose and the back of your head five or six times, first one and then the other, while facing your Vivaxis. Stand erect during this procedure and press very firmly. Drop your hands and allow the Force Flow 3 energies to flow in. This energy flow may take up to twenty seconds. Many people feel these energies as a vibration or energy flow through their head.

7 Turn ninety degrees to the left in the Southern Hemisphere, ninety degrees right in the Northern Hemisphere. Your ears are now in line with the Vivaxis. Repeat the stimulation of receptors but this time press the receptors above the ears. Then drop your hands and allow the energies to flow in.

8 Exercise briefly on all force flows to balance energies and ground off excess energy by pressing your hands for a few seconds on neutral ground.

After this exercise, your memory receptors will remain stimulated for about twenty minutes. To check, place your testing finger on a memory receptor and your recording arm should move without any visualisation or humming process.

Remember to use your testing finger because it will differentiate the force flow energy from ion flow which is recorded by the middle finger. In other words, you cannot test receptors using your middle finger as this would just give the usual response to ion flow both before and after the stimulation.

Another less specific way for stimulating memory receptors is to channel to the Vivaxis on Force Flow 3 while humming a nursery rhyme learnt in childhood. This stimulation relates to the strong connection between the healthy memory bars and rhymes during early childhood. Singing these rhymes restores the original healthy pattern in the receptors.

TESTING YOUR VISION

The eyes are an area of prime importance for health and well-being. For eye problems, we need to test all the receptors around each eye to see if there is a good response to the elements. Any dead spots should receive applications of energised water and should be jarred before channelling.

There may of course be other disturbed head receptors in relation to sight. It is interesting to know that the centre of one pupil will respond to a vertical chromium flow and the other to a horizontal one. In addition to our energy work with the eyes, we need to have the appropriate minerals and vitamins in our diet.

The natural vision exercises based on the Bates method[4] can be combined with this energy work. Fran agreed with the Natural Vision practitioners who recommend that time spent wearing spectacles be kept to a minimum. She found that the minerals in the spectacles disturbed the vision over a period of time due to the fact that the spectacle-wearer is constantly receiving frequencies through their eyes from the minerals in the glass. These minerals are present as part of the manufacturing process.

The Natural Vision therapists find that the more we rely on spectacles, the weaker the eyes become. Generally, it has been found that Vivaxis channelling, the use of the energised water and correction of any disturbed receptors around the eye can all improve eyesight.

Fran Nixon found that our near vision is connected with magnesium receptors and far vision with phosphorus receptors. These receptors are found just inside the bony orbit of the eye. The key elements for eyesight are located at these receptor sites and the positions of these elements are reversed for each eye. (You will remember that the key elements on the fingers were reversed for each hand.) One eye will be found to have magnesium receptors across the top and phosphorus underneath, while the positions will be reversed for the other eye.[5]

In my naturopathic practice, we use magnesium phosphate which is a combination of both magnesium and phosphorus in one of the twelve tissue salts. It is the main tissue salt for stress and the naturopathic understanding of short sight is that the muscles and ligaments controlling the eyeball are in a state of tension. We find we need this salt for our clients more than any other combination for all types of body stress.

1 Place the tip of your recording finger just inside the bony orbit below one eye to determine the position for the minerals around each eye. Visualise magnesium and note if there is a response in the recording hand. If not, move the recording finger to the bony

orbit above the eye and re-test. Make a chart for the positions of magnesium and phosphorus above and below each eye.

2 While scanning the ground in front of your feet, lightly place your index finger on a magnesium receptor and move your eyes gradually further away. At a distance of between 5–6 metres (15–20 feet) – perhaps less for very short-sighted people – your recording arm will cut out and the phosphorus vibration will take over. This means that you will need to move your testing finger to a phosphorus receptor to obtain further response in your recording arm. Continue the scanning process for far sight in that way. Mark the ground where magnesium cuts out and compare it later with the other eye.

3 Repeat for the other eye remembering that the position of the elements is reversed. You may find that your eyes differ in their response to the elements as it is common to have one eye with shorter or longer sight than the other (see Diagram 23).

Diagram 23

TESTING YOUR VISION

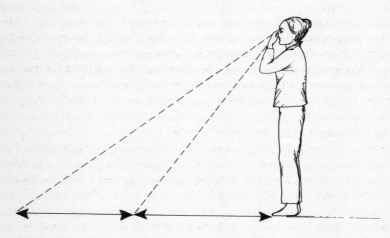

The bony orbit around the eye has frequencies of magnesium and phosphorus—one element is above and one below. The positions for these elements are reversed from one eye to the other.
• Close vision—your recording arm responds to visualisation of magnesium.
• Far vision—your recording arm responds to phosphorus.

USING SODA AND SALT TO CREATE A BALANCED ENVIRONMENT

A section of Fran Nixon's early writing was devoted to exploring what she called the Areahola forces. During one of her lecture tours in the United States, the atmosphere in California was found to be so disturbed that she nearly cancelled her seminar. She awoke on the morning before the seminar with the idea of correcting this atmospheric static by using the same elements which can be used in the bath for treating our own static.[6]

A positive atmosphere can be created which extends up to 13 metres (40 feet) or more by placing an open jar of sea salt and a jar of sodium bicarbonate in an east/west line about 20 cm (8 inches) apart. A force emerges from between the jars in a vertical stream. It balances the surrounding atmosphere and can also be used to enhance and balance our energies. In particular, this force gives our adrenal glands some beneficial stimulation.

Fran found that the Areahola forces are related to the wave behaviour of light in conjunction with the gravitational forces that control the tides. For instance if the jars of soda and salt are placed in a dark room no force field is generated. Fran also discovered that in the Northern Hemisphere, when the light vectors or waves come from the north and east they come up from the ground and enter the body through the feet and legs. In contrast, when the light comes from the south and west it comes down towards the ground from above. In the Southern Hemisphere I have found the reverse so that when light comes from south and west the forces come up from the ground. Most of the time the light vectors travel towards the jars in a narrow stream.

It was found that the forces carried by light in our environment can be drawn in by the soda and salt when placed in the east/west orientation. It appeared logical that because the jars needed to be placed west and east, the forces would be drawn in from north and south. Fran postulated that the reason the soda and sea salt carried these forces from north and south was related to the frequencies which flow from those directions (remember, we visualise the sodium frequency to find magnetic north). It appears that light is the carrier wave for these north and south forces.

The movement and change in direction of the light vectors through the days and months coincides with changes in the tides. Therefore the jars of soda and salt have to be placed in different positions according to whether it is a solunar flow time, high or low tide or new or full moons. At the high and low tides and during the new and full moon there are many variations in the direction of the light vectors and it is not a suitable time to use the Areahola forces.

Diagram 24

USING THE AREAHOLA FORCE FOR ENERGISING AND BALANCING

These diagrams are for the Southern Hemisphere. Reverse all directions including the hand for Northern Hemisphere.

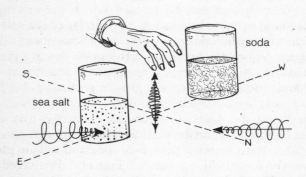

One force field accompanying the light is flowing down at an angle from the east and one from the north. These are the usual light directions during solunar flow times and both directions are from above and downwards.

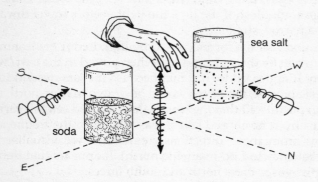

One force field is flowing up in an angle from west and the other from south. These are the most common directions during high and low tides and also full and new moons. However, at these times the force fields may change direction and it is not a stable time for doing the exercise.

This method should only be used by people who can test directions of energies or vectors so that they know how to position the jars (see Diagram 24).

It is best to use the Areahola forces when the light comes from the east and north in the Southern Hemisphere and south and west in the Northern Hemisphere. At these times, the jars should be arranged with the sea salt to the east and soda to the west in the Southern Hemisphere and sea salt to the west and soda to the east in the Northern Hemisphere. These are the usual positions for solunar flow times and correspond to the energies flowing down from above.

In the Northern Hemisphere, when light comes from the north or east, the sea salt is east of the soda which is therefore placed west. In the Southern Hemisphere this position is reversed and the sea salt is placed west of the soda. These are the usual positions for the jars during the high and low tides and during new and full moons. At these times the forces come up from the ground but in terms of compass directions can also come from all directions. It is not a stable time to take in the positive forces for our energy enhancement because the directions needed for placing the soda and salt may change quickly.

The correct position at any particular time can be tested by placing the centre of the palm over the centre point between the jars with fingers pointing north if you are in the Southern Hemisphere and south if in the Northern Hemisphere. If the Areahola forces are present your recording arm will follow the compass direction dictated by the brain as always happens if your brain receptors are in good working order. If the recording arm does not respond we know that the correct force flow is not present and we should switch the jars over. When the jars are in the correct position, the skin on your testing hand feels smooth after you have held your palm above the area between the jars. When the energies are disturbed, your hand feels sticky.

With correct positioning of the jars, the non-Areahola or static forces in an environment are drawn into the ground below the area of the jars. This appears to be the reason why a disturbed atmosphere can be corrected. It is very important that the jars are always placed on the ground floor of any building in which they are used. If for instance, they are placed on the floor of the second storey of any building, the non-Areahola forces will form a static field in the area below the jars, in this case on the ground floor level, leaving only the floors above with an atmosphere which is free from static.

The extent of the field emanating from the jars diminishes over time. The size of the field in the static room can be tested by scanning away from the jars, visualising a compass direction and establishing that your arm follows the direction of thought. When the force field has dissipated and static returns, your arm will move at right angles to the direction of thought. The soda has gradually absorbed the static energies and will no longer emit a healthy energy field. It should be discarded at that point. The salt can be recharged by leaving it in sunshine for a few hours. This will actually enlarge the size of the healthy force field. When not in use, the materials should be kept at different levels in a dark cupboard.

CHARGING THE BODY WITH THE AREAHOLA FORCES

Originally, the absorption of the Areahola forces was the most lasting and effective method of clearing one's energy circuit including erasure of foreign influences. In addition, the immune system was enhanced through strengthening the energy circuits. The technique of channelling on the force flows has largely replaced the need for this exercise but it could be useful at times when we are unable to use the force flows due to our location or to extreme weather conditions.

1 Place containers of soda and salt in the correct directions of east and west according to the previous instructions.

2 Bring blood to all your head receptors by hanging your head down for about eight seconds. Stand clear of the jars during this time.

3 Lift your head and immediately hold the palm of your right hand over the centre point between jars for about six seconds to absorb Areahola forces. Breathe deeply. Repeat with your left hand. Remember to hold your fingers in the right direction according to whether you are north or south of the equator (point your fingers towards north for Southern Hemisphere and south for Northern Hemisphere).

4 Now expose each finger and thumb in turn to the Areahola forces between the jars for about six seconds.

5 Jog around the room for about one minute to spread Areahola energies to your foot receptors.

6 Do the short form of the neutralising exercise on page 18 for
   about six cycles to further spread the energies throughout the
   body.

An interesting side experiment can be made by placing a lump of
white sugar into the jar of sea salt. You'll find that no energies can
be recorded between the jars and they no longer have any positive
effect on a static room. This illustrates the effect of refined food and
especially refined sugar on our energies.

During the years I worked with Fran, she no longer taught this
process because her work with the energy layers had taken over
and was found to be generally more useful and convenient.
However, the technique is obviously of great value for a room,
office or conference centre where a disturbed atmosphere has
formed due to the lighting, air conditioning or other factors.

Creating a Compatible Wave Field for the Home or Office

Fran found that a consistently compatible and health-giving field
could be maintained, despite changes in light direction, by the
following arrangement of salt and soda. Two sealed jars of soda are
placed 15 cm (6 inches) in an east/west direction outside the house.
The jars are placed on a bed of charcoal on ground which is slightly
lower than the floor of the lowest room. The sealed jar of salt is
placed 2 metres (6 feet) away and one metre (3 feet) higher than the
soda. The compatible field will extend about 180 metres (600 feet)
in all directions and the soda does not deteriorate for many months.
Any area below the jars is not included in the compatible field. The
field only operates in daylight. Keep any other jars of soda and salt
in a dark cupboard so that conflicting wave fields are not formed.

7

TESTING OUR ENERGY RECEPTORS

★ ★ ★ ★ ★ ★

W E HAVE already examined some of the receptors on our fingers and discovered that they respond to the frequencies of chromium, iron, zinc and iodine. These frequencies are connected to our Vivaxis. In addition, we have tested our triple groups which are the lines of receptors down the back and front of the body. These receptors are also linked to our Vivaxis.

The first step in detecting energy imbalances or blockages in receptors is to test the ion flow in the area of concern. Remember this involves placing the tip of either middle finger on the part of the body to be tested. Normal ion flow produces a back and forth movement in the recording hand. But the recording hand may be non-responsive or moving in circles. This indicates an energy problem involving the receptors at that point.

Each receptor is linked to either a gland, organ, limb and so on. The chemistry associated with a particular part of the body produces a specific characteristic which is reflected in the wave pattern of its associated receptors. These wave frequencies have not yet been identified by medical science. A disturbed receptor is an energy contact point whose group of elements have developed an imbalance in part of their atomic structure which in turn affects the electromagnetic field. This produces the chaotic, circulating energy flow in your recording hand when your middle or ion flow testing finger is placed over the receptor.

In the following exercises, we are testing receptors which have specific functions in the body. Therefore we need to use the correct testing finger which will be the index finger of the left hand if above the Vivaxis and ring finger if below for testing all areas on the body above the navel. Reverse these fingers for testing areas below the navel.

The categories of receptors include the following main groups:

1 Triple groups – these groups run in vertical lines down the back and front of the body. The receptors are all oriented towards our Vivaxis and associated with mineral frequencies.

2 Lower brain receptor groups – these groups are associated with mathematical thought and are primarily located on the head below the hairline (see Diagram 25). They consist of twenty-four groups each comprised of three receptors. The central receptor in the group responds to mathematical thought. In addition, there is:

• An involuntary receptor located immediately to one side of the central brain receptor. These receptors have a similar role to the triple groups and can be related to the traditional Chinese meridian system. They govern the automatic function of all organs hence the name 'involuntary'. These receptors, like those in the triple groups, are oriented to the Vivaxis and they have both a horizontal and vertical wave (see Diagram 1).

• A voluntary receptor the same distance on the other side of the central brain receptor. These receptors are associated with move-ment of the body and communication with our environment. They have only a horizontal wave which is associated with the object in our environment under consideration. They are not connected with our Vivaxis.

3 Higher brain receptor groups – these groups are associated with memory, creative thought patterns and energies from the sun and moon. They are located over the crown of the head above the hairline (see Diagram 25). On one side of the central higher brain receptor is a sun receptor and on the other side a moon receptor.

4 Specialised receptors – this type of receptor is associated with particular organs such as eye, ear, tongue, pancreas and so on. These specialised receptors are not only found near the organ concerned but also on other parts of the body. For instance, there are adrenal receptors at the end of each eyebrow. A number of

Diagram 25

LOWER BRAIN RECEPTOR GROUPS

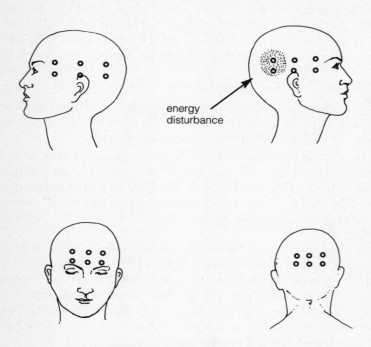

energy
disturbance

HIGHER BRAIN RECEPTOR GROUPS

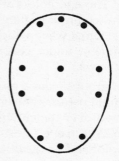

organs also have associated receptors on the ends of the fingers and toes and this corresponds with the traditional Chinese meridian system where there are end points for each organ system on the ends of the digits.

The network of receptors covers your entire head, neck and body. If your voluntary receptors for movement are disturbed, wave messages to limbs and reflexes are also disrupted. If your involuntary receptors associated with organs are disturbed, you will have a physiological disturbance of organ function and so on. When any receptors are disturbed the associated physiology and organ function suffers and this scenario eventually leads to organic disease. Healthy, balanced receptors act like tiny transformers for energy throughout the body.

IDENTIFYING THE LOWER BRAIN RECEPTOR GROUPS

These brain receptors are described in point 2 above. There is the central brain receptor associated with mathematical thought.[1] On one side of the central brain receptor is an involuntary receptor with energies flowing to and fro between our Vivaxis and ourselves. The voluntary receptor on the other side will only have a horizontal wave which moves towards any object we focus on in the environment. The receptors are about 0.5 cm ($1/4$ inch) from each other. The side receptors swap their function depending on our position in relation to our Vivaxis. We started to explore this phenomenon of switching when testing the alternating spin in the triple groups of receptors.

Testing the Lower Brain Receptors

The twenty-four lower brain receptor groups are shown in Diagram 25. Each of these groups contains the three receptor types. Because these receptors are very close to each other we need to use our testing finger carefully to differentiate each type. To do this we just use the tip of our fingernail to test each type within the group of three.

The central brain receptors (lower and higher) are the only type of receptors on your head that are stimulated by mathematical exercises. Locate a brain receptor by moving your testing finger down the central line of your forehead while thinking of a simple multiplication (e.g. $2 \times 2 = 4$). Half-way down your forehead you will come to a brain receptor and your recording arm will move back and forth. If the receptor is disturbed your hand will move in a circular movement.

To test the other receptors move your testing finger slightly to the left or right. Your recording arm will move towards your Vivaxis if you are touching the involuntary receptor. Now move your finger to the other side of the central receptor and concentrate on an object in the room. Your recording arm will move in the direction of the object only when you are touching a voluntary receptor. Remember, this type of receptor makes a temporary horizontal link with the object of your thought. Now take up the opposite direction in terms of your Vivaxis and note that the two receptors just tested will reverse their roles.

These receptors on either side of the central brain receptor have alternating spins, one with a clockwise motion and the other with a counter-clockwise motion. This can be checked by first finding a central brain receptor on your forehead, then moving your testing finger slightly to the right while holding your recording hand like a fist with the thumb stuck upwards. Your hand will circle in one direction which will reverse if you turn so that you face the opposite direction in relation to your Vivaxis. The receptor on the left-hand side can then be checked and will be found to have the opposite spin.

EXAMINING THE HIGHER BRAIN RECEPTORS

Each of these twelve receptor groups above the hairline measures one centimetre (^{1}/$_2$ inch) across (see Diagram 25). To find a higher brain receptor conduct a simple mental exercise as you did to find the lower brain receptors. These receptors are also stimulated by recalling an incident from the past, or by thinking of your Vivaxis. To find the sun receptor, visualise the sun and move the tip of the recording fingernail to the left or right of the central receptor until there is a response in the recording arm. The opposite side will then give a response to the moon. These side receptors will reverse their wavelengths for sun and moon as the sun and moon change their positions in relation to the earth each day.

Brain receptors must be in good working order before we can effectively use the brain and receive earth energies. Dysfunction can be caused by earthquakes, electric storms, magnetic disturbances, electrical equipment including diagnostic equipment in hospitals and clinics, television, computer terminals, fluorescent lights and many other sources which emit electromagnetic frequencies.

Five particular brain receptors apart from those discussed give distress signals in response to these causes. Two receptors are positioned in the centre points of the ears, two more are in the same line at the centre of the nose and back of the head, and one is on top of the head (see Diagram 26). If you hold your testing finger on these points your recording hand may move in a circular direction or in a direction at right angles to your Vivaxis.

A simple exercise will show us how these five brain receptors can become temporarily affected so that our Vivaxis appears to be at right angles to its true direction. Use your testing finger to find one of these receptors while standing on neutral ground during solunar flow period, and note how your arm immediately swings in the direction of your Vivaxis. Then stand under any type of light which is switched on. Within a few seconds you will find that your arm swings at right angles to the true direction of your Vivaxis.[2] If you have been subjected to electromagnetic interference for some hours or days, this disturbance can remain until you correct the disturbed receptors by jarring and then channelling to your Vivaxis while standing on a force flow.

EXERCISE TO TEST THE BRAIN GROUPS

This is a method Fran Nixon devised for testing brain groups to check that their receptors are in good working order and not disturbed by static, foreign fields, drugs, chemicals or psychological stress.

1 Prepare as for channelling by removing spectacles, jewellery, watches, tight clothing and shoes unless they have leather or rubber soles.

2 Do the short form of neutralising exercise.

Diagram 26

BRAIN RECEPTORS AFFECTED BY STATIC

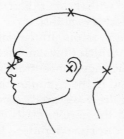

Brain receptors at these points register static and this is evidenced by a circulating motion in the recording hand. Our Vivaxis channel also appears at right-angles to its normal position.

3 Hold your spine erect and your head level; keep your feet well apart and eyes open.

4 Turn in a full circle without visualising any particular direction. Allow your arm to move towards your Vivaxis. As you turn, different receptors on your head will link towards your Vivaxis and if any are disturbed, you will find that your arm will not move towards your Vivaxis when the receptors are facing in that direction.

5 To find the disturbed receptor you will probably need to systematically use the testing finger to test each of the brain receptors on the disturbed quadrant of the head. This means doing a simple mathematical calculation to find the points shown on Diagram 25 and noting which receptors give a disturbed circular motion in the recording arm.

Correction of Disturbed Receptors

Since you now know how to find the energy layers you can correct any disturbed receptor. Stand on the selected force flow, preferably Force Flow 1 or 3 and face in the direction of your Vivaxis. Jar the disturbed receptor strongly with the heel of your hand with your head tilted out of the Vivaxis channel. Then channel in the usual manner to restore energies to the receptor.

COMMUNICATION WITH OUR ENVIRONMENT

Before we discuss the way communication occurs via the voluntary receptors, remember that one receptor in the lower brain receptor group responds to our two Vivaxis forces, horizontal and vertical. This is the involuntary receptor which is related to all the automatic functions of our organs. Fran Nixon called these receptors involuntary because they are involved with the meridians that control the function of the liver, pancreas, kidneys and so on.

Voluntary receptors are connected to our immediate environment. They emit a horizontal wave which flows in the direction of the object, place or person on which we concentrate at any particular time. These receptors respond to the command of our brain or to the command of another brain if we are under hypnosis. Normally, when our thought ceases, the horizontal wave no longer communicates with the subject under consideration. However, it can become linked permanantly with another Vivaxis which then adds a foreign vertical wave. In such a case, the whole meridian to which this receptor is linked will be affected.[3]

This more detrimental link can occur through magnets, hypnotism, or diagnostic and treatment machines with a pulsed wave and sometimes through body work where a therapist holds bilateral meridians for more than a few seconds.

SPECIAL COMMUNICATION CENTRES

The left index finger used for recording when we are above our Vivaxis is intimately related to a special communication centre on the left temple. This receptor site is interesting because the speech centre is in this part of the brain. I have yet to research whether an individual below their Vivaxis has their ring finger related to this communication centre on the left temple. Another important communication centre is found between the thyroid gland and thymus where the two breast bones meet. These special communication centres contain extra receptors including some linked to the eyes and the heart. They also have a central brain receptor but in this case it has double pairs of receptors on either side.

A very significant communication centre is located at the centre point on top of your head. The receptor on the left of this centre has an ear receptor in front. The receptor on the right has an eye receptor in front. At the centre point itself is a respiratory receptor with a brain receptor located front and back of this receptor.[4] There is a corresponding centre just beyond the back of the hard palate on the roof of the mouth. All these points need to be tested for people who have diseases like multiple sclerosis or Meniere's disease. This communication centre is in line with the hypothalamus which is the organ controlling the nervous system.

During the major period or high tide, the receptors on top of your head become stimulated during daylight by the light flowing vertically down upon them (see Diagram 27). This in turn stimulates the receptor associated with our appetite for food and especially influences the digestion of protein. Incidentally, it is a proven fact that fishing is most successful at high tide because that is when the fish are also hungry.

The communication centre on your left temple is connected to lymph glands under your left arm. Linking too strongly to another person through fear or worry can cause these lymph glands to be permanently linked to another person because a foreign Vivaxis is created. The immune system will then be at risk which may well

Diagram 27

THE STIMULUS OF APPETITE RECEPTORS FOR FOOD AND SEX

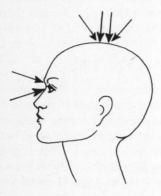

- The larger arrows indicate the sex receptors and are associated with chromium horizontal groups.

- The smaller arrows indicate the food receptors and are associated with selenium.

account for diseases such as cancer manifesting after a person has linked negatively with another person for some time. This is obviously only one contributing factor.

It is easy to understand how our memory, the way we relate to other people, and our internal commnication from brain to limb will be profoundly disturbed if a foreign Vivaxis is feeding into any of the receptors involved with our communication centres. It appears that in health we have considerable immunity to outside energy fields but through accident, infection, stress, negative thoughts and feelings, or through biochemical disturbances, we are vulnerable to other sources of energy being introduced into our circuits. In the case of a foreign wave from another person or from an electro-magnetic source, some receptors in the communication centre will link to this foreign source and some will stay linked to our Vivaxis.

TESTING THE RECEPTORS FOR MOVEMENT

Specific receptors in the brain groups are associated with each movable part of the body. The voluntary receptors in the brain groups concerned with a particular part of the body will respond when that body part is in action. As the brain instructs a part to move, a wave train moves along a definite path from a voluntary brain receptor to a particular receptor associated with that body part.

Try this for yourself by testing your knee movement. First find a brain receptor on your forehead by doing a simple calculation until your recording arm moves. Find the voluntary receptor at one side of that brain receptor. Then flex your knee while moving your testing finger lightly along the track as shown in Diagram 28 until your recording hand stops. This will be the knee receptor. The track will probably vary depending on your position relative to your Vivaxis but if the knee receptor is disturbed, you will observe a circular motion in your recording hand as your testing finger moves along the track.[5]

Testing the movement in any part of the body is a fairly tedious business of finding the track on your cranium associated with the body part. Each limb is connected to specific receptors in one of the four quadrants of the head. For correcting energy blocks in specific areas it is also necessary to find the associated terminal points on your fingers and toes as they may be disturbed. Obviously, an assistant tester will be needed in some cases when you are testing the receptors on the ends of fingers and toes as we do not have three hands which would be needed to test those points on ourselves!

In relation to knee movement, one brain and knee receptor will be associated with forward movement, one pair with backward movement, one pair for upward motion and the final pair for downward motion. These pairs will swap their functions depending on the direction we face. It is easy to imagine the corrective

Diagram 28

THE PATHWAYS FROM A BRAIN RECEPTOR TO KNEE RECEPTOR

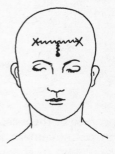 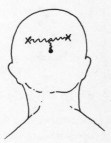

work which could be done in cases of paralysis if these basic techniques were accepted in medicine. Fran described some cases where she retrained paralysed people to walk again after helping them to find and correct their disturbed receptors. One case involved a young boy who had been involved in a gunshot accident.[6]

Tongue Receptors

There are many receptors on the tongue associated with body movement and function. No doubt this is why Chinese medicine uses the tongue for diagnosis. There are also a number of receptors on the right side of the nose associated with tongue movement. Lightly touch these receptors with your testing finger while moving your tongue in and out of your mouth. Your recording hand will register a strong response. If you test the left side of your nose nothing happens. You can locate receptors for tongue movement on your nose, your head and also on your toes and fingers. If your tongue was paralysed after for example an accident or cerebral vascular accident, these receptors would need to be found and corrected (see Diagram 29).

Diagram 29

RECEPTORS DOWN THE TONGUE

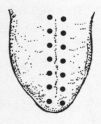

Half have a clockwise motion and half a counter-clockwise motion.

Wave Link to Vivaxis

A wave link connecting to our Vivaxis appears to be the reason why brain receptors can control the direction of movement for the various parts of the body. When you face your Vivaxis channel you are like a radio set which has been tuned to your specific frequency (see Diagram 30).[7]

Diagram 30

WAVE VECTORS WHEN ALIGNED (A) AND NOT ALIGNED (B) TO THE VIVAXIS CHANNEL

(A)

(B)

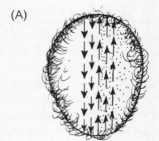
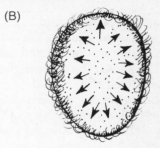

(A) Direction of wave vectors with your head level and aligned with Vivaxis. The energies run side by side in opposite directions which change at the midline of your skull.

(B) Directions of vectors when not aligned showing the scattered effect.

Receptors in the Mouth

Every part of your body appears to be represented by receptors in some part of the mouth. For instance, the two vital receptors located on either side of the top of the head have their associated receptors on the roof of the mouth at the back of the soft palate. As mentioned these are in direct line with that key to the central nervous system called the hypothalamus.[8] Another relationship exists between the tip of the tongue and the base of the spine. In cases of severe pain or disability in any part of the body, improvement will only be temporary until all the associated receptors are found.

An interesting test can be performed by visualising a favourite food as you move your sensing finger down the centre of your tongue. When you get to the food or appetite receptor, your recording arm will move strongly. There is also a sex receptor nearby which can be tested by visualising enjoyable sex! Areas on the tongue for the fingers and toes can be found by concentrating on these digits. These correspondences between receptors and our inner organs provide the reason why so many practitioners and clients find value and healing through body work. Massage and acupressure must stimulate many internal organs and tissues during the course of treatment.

FURTHER WORK WITH RECEPTORS ON THE HEAD

The Adrenal Glands

There are points at the end of each eyebrow which are associated with the adrenal glands. The adrenal glands sit on top of your kidneys. They are associated with your energy levels and are affected by stress. The adrenal gland receptors emit the frequencies of the elements copper and selenium. Using your testing finger touch the end of one eyebrow and visualise first copper and then selenium to find the positions of these elements on the end of each eyebrow. If the end of one eyebrow records the frequency of copper, the other end will register selenium. The positions on the other eyebrow will be reversed. Record the positions as you did for the fingertips.

If there is a disturbance in these glands you may observe a circulating movement in your recording hand when touching the receptors and visualising the appropriate element. Correct this disturbance with the usual technique of jarring and channelling.

There are also selenium and copper receptors on the top of your head and on the soles of your feet. The selenium receptors on the head and copper receptors on the feet are activated at the low tide and that is why you should channel for selenium at this time for enhanced immunity. At the high tide there is a reversal and the copper receptors on your head and selenium on your feet are stimulated. Fran found that the selenium frequency relates to protein metabolism and copper to carbohydrate metabolism. On this basis, one wonders whether candida sufferers have disturbed copper receptors.

The Thyroid and Parathyroid Glands

The thyroid gland is situated in front of the larynx or voice box and the parathyroids are found embedded in the four corners of the thyroid. These are important structures to check for disturbances. The thyroid is connected with our metabolic activities and the parathyroids with the balance of calcium. Iodine and chromium receptors are located on the thyroid and the parathyroids will have frequencies of carbon, calcium and silicon. The position of these elements will vary from person to person but two of the parathyroids will emit calcium frequencies and two will emit carbon. I have found the iodine receptors to be in numerous places across the surface of the thyroid gland. You can test this fact by visually scanning the thyroid of another person while thinking of iodine.

The Jaw

Receptors on one side of the jaw relate to the magnetic group with iron as the main element and those on the other side are associated with the gravitational group which features zinc or iodine. The positions of the elements reverse at the centre line of both upper and lower jaw.

The Cobalt Receptors

The cobalt receptors form a band around your head with a vertical wave on one side and a horizontal wave on the other. Cobalt is one of the elements associated with Force Flow 1, and these receptors often become disturbed from the effects of television. Here is a small research exercise we can do with our children – determine how much television they can watch before their cobalt receptors become disturbed. The distance from the set would also need to be taken into account. As oxygen is the mate of cobalt on Force Flow 1, there are also oxygen receptors around the head near the cobalt band.

Inert Gases

Receptors for the inert gases (e.g. hydrogen, ozone and chlorine) have been found fairly recently in a diagonal line beginning in front

Diagram 31

GAS RECEPTORS ON THE SIDE OF THE FOREHEAD

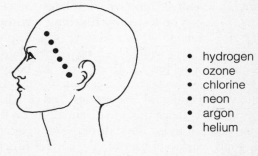

- hydrogen
- ozone
- chlorine
- neon
- argon
- helium

of the ear, moving up to the temple area (see Diagram 31). The inert gases are only recently being considered as having a role to play in healthy human functioning. More research will need to be done before the significance of these frequencies is understood in relation to our health.

TESTING THE RECEPTORS FOR MEMORY AND IMAGINATION

It appears that all our body functions have their associated receptors. Finding disturbances in these receptors such as those for memory will obviously be significant in conditions like attention deficit syndrome in children and in types of dementia including people suffering from Alzheimer's disease. I believe it is likely that correcting disturbed memory receptors in elderly people could alleviate their memory problems.

Our magnetic group of receptors corresponds to memory and therefore we touch or look at one of the iron-based groups when memorising and note the movement of our recording hand. To initially find an iron-based group, visualise iron while lightly moving the testing finger down one side of the forehead. Alternatively look at a fingertip which has the iron group.

Our imagination is related to the gravitational group. This is not surprising when you consider the relationship between the element zinc and the gonads, and between iodine and the thyroid which is associated with creative pursuits (see fuller explanation in the next chapter). To test your imagination, note the movement in your recording hand as you touch a gravitational group which will always contain either iodine or zinc, or just look at the iodine or zinc fingertip while using your imagination.

Logical or linear thinking stimulates our horizontal chromium groups while creative thinking stimulates the vertical chromium receptors. This can be tested by touching a chromium horizontal group on the forehead while counting or multiplying, or thinking of something creative while touching a vertical group.

In summary, you have learned how all body functions, both voluntary and involuntary, are associated with receptors which are related to various mineral frequencies. You can diagnose disturbed receptors and rebalance them by channelling on the force flows. In particular, you can assess the state of the brain receptors which need to be in good working order for the correct functioning of all the body organs via the meridian system.

8

GLANDS, CHAKRAS AND FORCE FLOWS

* * * * * *

A
S THE earth turns on its axis and aligns in different ways with the sun, moon, and constellations which form the zodiac, we are presented with opportunites for increased spiritual alignment. There are also relationships between our spiritual organs, the chakras, their associated glands and the energy flows on our planet.

The relationship between the earth and humanity, and the health of the individual, is highlighted by a study of the glands and their associated chakras or energy centres. The endocrine glands are a most important part of our physical body as they regulate many bodily functions. In turn, there are many minerals and vitamins important for the health of the endocrine glands. If there are disturbed receptors related to these substances, uptake of vitamins and minerals will be impaired. For healthy endocrine glands, we need to have a free flow of energy from the earth via the Vivaxis flows to the mineral receptors on all parts of the body.

In this chapter we will look at the esoteric or subjective basis for the endocrine glands and most of the chakras or energy centres. The head chakras and their associated glands will be discussed in the next chapter. We have seven endocrine glands comprising the adrenals, pancreas, gonads, thyroid, thymus, pituitary and pineal. An endocrine gland produces a hormonal secretion which goes directly into the bloodstream. Some glands such as the pancreas produce both exocrine and endocrine substances. The exocrine secretion from the pancreas is pancreatic juice which flows into the digestive tract; insulin is the endocrine secretion which circulates in the bloodstream to keep sugar levels balanced. Each endocrine gland therefore performs a vital physical function which has been recognised as an expression of more subtle energy in spiritual teachings down the ages.

The wisdom teaching from the East which comes from beyond the Himalayas (Trans-Himalayan teaching) has been given to the West by several teachers in written form. The basic teaching in this area concerns the correlation of the endocrine glands with energy centres in the etheric body. These centres are often known as chakras ('chakra' is a Sanskrit word meaning wheel). The most detailed information to date on this subject is in Alice Bailey's book *Esoteric Healing* which explains the relationship between the glands and the chakras.[1]

The chakras are the mechanism for transmitting our spiritual impulses, thoughts, and emotions to our physical brain consciousness. They appear to act like electrical transformers which transduce subtle energies into a suitable form for conditioning and influencing our glands. The energies received by our physical body will vary according to our state of consciousness.

The chakras not only manifest at the subtle level underlying the physical which we call the etheric, but have counterparts at other levels such as our astral/emotional nature and mental levels. We have already considered how our several levels of consciousness interpenetrate each other; remember the analogy involving the mixture of sand, water and air. This analogy is not perfect because sand, water and air are all physical but the concept can be extended to energy fields at subtle levels. In relation to the glands, we can now devise a flow chart which shows some of the subtle levels which affect our health:

soul → mind → emotions → etheric → triple groups/meridians → nerve plexi → glands → blood → tissues

Disease can occur when we have a problem, blockage or imbalance at any of these levels because the endocrine glands can suffer from disturbances in any part of this chain. The exciting work on psycho-neuro-immunology (PNI) indicates that the nervous system, immune system and hormonal activity is profoundly affected by our mental and emotional life.[2] This fairly recent research in part confirms Alice Bailey's assertion that up to ninety per cent of disease has subtle psychological and etheric causes. The techniques discussed in this book are all focussed at the etheric level as it interfaces with the electromagnetic fields of the body.

We must always consider the conditioning effect of the emotions and mind on the etheric field. In working with people using the techniques described in this book, it quickly became apparent to me that emotional disturbance immediately affects the energy field and its strength, and also the ability of a person to accurately record energies.

A detailed analysis of the chakras and endocrine glands is given in my book *Meditation, The Most Natural Therapy*.[3] An abbreviated description is included here for the purpose of understanding the relationship of the chakras and glands with the energy layers on our planet. The main seven chakras are each related to a level of consciousness (see Diagram 32). As transformers in an electrical sense, they step down the energy from the various planes so that we can receive it safely into our physical brain consciousness and nervous system.

Basically, the main chakras operate in pairs and this is how I have found them to be reflected on the energy layers of the earth. We will first look at the gonads (ovaries and testes) which are related to the sacral chakra. This chakra and the higher counterpart, the throat chakra, with its endocrine gland, the thyroid, are linked with Force Flow 4. Some of the key minerals associated with these glands are zinc and iodine, and these mineral frequencies are transmitted by Force Flow 4.

Iodine is the main mineral required by the thyroid for healthy functioning; zinc is a key element needed by the gonads. The link between the gonads and zinc was established many decades ago after clinical trials with this mineral produced secondary sexual characteristics in male dwarfs. Zinc is also an important supplement for infertility caused by low sperm count.[4] When we are assessing whether minerals are disturbed in the body, we can monitor a person on the energy flows at those levels where the minerals occur (this is detailed in chapter 10). In relation to the sacral and throat chakras, we will monitor zinc, iodine, and other associated minerals.

THE SACRAL CHAKRA

The sacral chakra is concerned mainly with our appetite for food, sex, and other physical comforts. It was obviously very active in

Diagram 32

POSITIVE QUALITIES EXPRESSED BY THE CHAKRAS

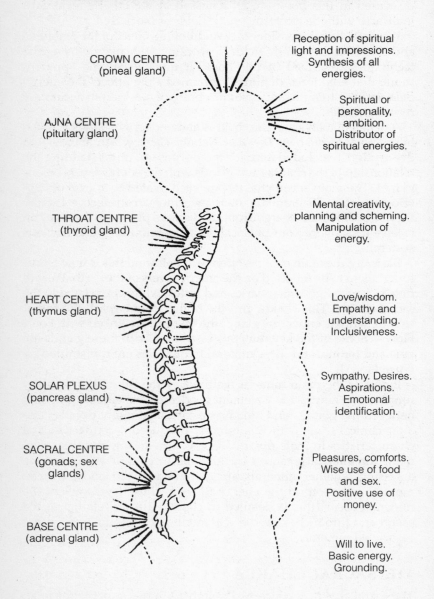

CROWN CENTRE
(pineal gland)

Reception of spiritual
light and impressions.
Synthesis of all
energies.

AJNA CENTRE
(pituitary gland)

Spiritual or
personality,
ambition.
Distributor of
spiritual energies.

THROAT CENTRE
(thyroid gland)

Mental creativity,
planning and scheming.
Manipulation of
energy.

HEART CENTRE
(thymus gland)

Love/wisdom.
Empathy and
understanding.
Inclusiveness.

SOLAR PLEXUS
(pancreas gland)

Sympathy. Desires.
Aspirations.
Emotional
identification.

SACRAL CENTRE
(gonads; sex
glands)

Pleasures, comforts.
Wise use of food
and sex.
Positive use of
money.

BASE CENTRE
(adrenal gland)

Will to live.
Basic energy.
Grounding.

primitive mankind who experienced little more in life than these essentials. There are very few humans today who function solely through this level of consciousness but we can see a definite correlation in domestic animals who are happy and content if adequately fed, housed and comforted. To inhibit the expression of their sexual instincts, we often have them neutered because this makes them even more domesticated and manageable.

Television advertisements are often very strongly pitched at the basic functions of the sacral chakra. They place an emphasis on the body beautiful, on food and on products which will increase our comfort. Providing ourselves with the most comfortable existence possible requires money and therefore the handling of money is intimately related to the balance of the sacral chakra. From an esoteric perspective, money is related to energy and is considered to be crystallised prana or energy. Hence the sacral chakra is associated with the handling of energy generally and to basic levels of energy which reside in the etheric body.

The sacral chakra is the psychic organ which is linked with our etheric body and by extension to the etheric body of the planet. Consequently all work with natural therapies which involves improving and balancing energies in plants, animals and humans involves working with etheric energies and the sacral chakra. In particular, Vivaxis energies are involved with the etheric level and therefore indirectly with the planetary and human sacral chakras. The base and spleen chakras are also intimately involved with physical and etheric energy.

People who are unable to handle money may have an imbalance at this sacral level. The planet itself has a gross sacral imbalance which is expressed as famine in some parts of the globe and over-abundance in others. The planetary sacral expression relates also to those subtle energies behind weather patterns and to extreme weather conditions found in some parts of the globe. Earthquakes and volcanoes are further examples of physical/etheric energy imbalances in the planet.

When the planetary sacral chakra is finally balanced it will coincide with a redistribution of wealth and planetary resources and to an improvement in health and housing for all the earth's inhabitants. It is a process which has hopefully begun already. We do seem to be taking more responsibility for people who are in need – the starving, homeless and uneducated people in each country. Our global economy which now has entities such as the International Monetary Fund, the World Bank, and other large multinational corporations is part of the planetary sacral chakra. The monitoring of wealth and spending is a strong aspect of our developing global village, an aspect of Gaia as a self-balancing entity.

Health problems associated with this chakra affect the gonads, the reproductive system in general and the associated tissues. These problems may include ovarian cysts and tumours, uterine fibroids and menstrual difficulties, infertility in both sexes, prostatitis and enlarged prostate in the male, cystitis, and cancer of any part of the reproductive system in either sex. Psychological sexual problems are also part of the functioning of the sacral chakra.

From an esoteric perspective, our health problems are caused by an imbalance of energy which means either over- or under-stimulation of the chakras. This imbalance may be influenced by our psyche, our environment including our heredity, and the relationship between the sacral centre and its higher counterpart, the throat chakra.

THE THROAT CHAKRA

The throat chakra is related to the expression of our thoughts and creativity. It has become very active in this century and the great interest we have in continuing education in all areas of life is evidence of this fact. The knowledge explosion has been concurrent with the growth of radio, television, satellite and computer network. These technological developments have made it possible to accelerate learning in every sphere of life. Thus the throat chakra expresses the developing mind within humanity and it is now very active in the global sense.

As the psychic organ for creativity, our throat chakra is involved with planning and producing creative work whether through writing, painting, building, gardening or any creative pursuit which we may follow. It corresponds with the development of mind power and is therefore much associated with design or, more unfortunately, with manipulation.

The throat chakra's associated endocrine gland is the thyroid which largely controls our metabolism. An overactive, concrete mind will overstimulate our throat chakra and this in turn stimulates the thyroid. We can become a person who is too speedy in every way. In extreme cases individuals may suffer from hyperthyroidism. The concrete mind is that aspect of our psyche which is concerned with all our mundane rather than creative activities.

The condition of hyperthyroidism, or overstimulation of the metabolic processes, leads to problems with weight loss, nervousness and irritability, tachycardia (fast heartbeat) and may sometimes cause a strain on the heart. If the throat chakra is too sluggish we may experience symptoms such as weight gain, slow and dull expression of thoughts, dry hair and skin and a general slowing down of all the metabolic processes, leading to tiredness and depression. In my clinical practice I often treat people for a subtle imbalance of the throat chakra although their blood tests may not show an imbalance in the thyroid. However, their symptoms of depression, exhaustion and mental sluggishness often disappear after herbal and homeopathic treatment to balance the thyroid.

There are other organs and tissues associated with the throat chakra including the bronchials and upper lungs, the shoulders and arms, and the lymphatic system. All lymphatic and catarrhal conditions such as bronchitis and asthma are associated with this energy centre or chakra.

As the throat chakra becomes active and creative thought is stimulated, it draws up energy from the sacral centre and a balance between the two centres is established. This gives us the capacity to control our appetites and energy in many ways. If this balance is not adequate, we may see an individual who has wild and interesting creative schemes but no way of grounding them in a practical sense. The sacral energy should be used to bring to fruition the creative schemes of the throat centre. It provides the energy and resources (e.g. money) for the enterprise.

To ensure that our creative works are for the good of the whole and not simply to satisfy our own ego and the need for fame and fortune, the energies from the sacral centre should pass through the heart on their way to the throat. People do tend to move through a stage of selfish creation. Many artists fall into this category although their works are often uplifting due to their sheer beauty. Artists may write, paint or compose for their own needs but the result is uplifting to humanity.

The most spiritual type of creativity answers a need, and this will often not fall into the category of art. For instance, it may be a new surgical procedure or apparatus which will give health to thousands. Other examples on a larger scale may be processes which purify the air, or water in our environment, or new processes which assist farming and food production.

THE SOLAR PLEXUS AND HEART CHAKRAS

Both the heart chakra and the solar plexus chakra are linked with Force Flow 3 – the magnetic band. You may remember that this band contains all those elements which conduct electricity: copper, iron, selenium, nickel, gold, silver, and sodium. The associated endocrine glands are the thymus gland (heart) and the pancreas (solar plexus). There is not an obvious connection between the minerals and the glands here, and I have pondered on the relationship.

It is interesting that Force Flow 3 is the band of energy that remains constant during both high and low tides and at all times during the year. Perhaps this reflects the central and important position the heart and its associated chakra play in our lives. In addition, consider the associated tissues and functions of the heart – copper and iron are both essential ingredients of the blood, while selenium is needed for good immunity and thus relates to the thymus gland. Furthermore, gold is the element which has alchemically always been linked with the heart. We even have a colloquial saying, 'she has a heart of gold'.

Silver is associated with the moon which has always been linked to our emotional life and it has its main gateway through the solar plexus chakra. Sodium is alkaline in effect and related to the pancreatic fluid which must neutralise the acid secreted by the stomach. Both silver and sodium frequencies are emitted by Force Flow 3. So we can see that there are some logical connections between the elements on Force Flow 3, the pancreas and thymus glands and the associated chakras.

The solar plexus is the psychic organ for the expression of energy from that plane or level of consciousness called the astral plane. In individuals it is the gateway to our astral body. It relates to our moods, feelings, desires, emotions and in its highest aspect, to our aspirations.

This chakra and its gland, the pancreas, governs all our digestive organs and processes. From an esoteric perspective, the many disturbances in this area suffered by mankind are due to under- or overstimulation of this chakra. We may find health problems include dyspepsia, stomach, duodenal and bowel ulcers, constipation, diarrhoea, gall stones, appendicitis, diverticulitis, pancreatitis, diabetes and cancer or tumours in any of these parts. When we consider how widespread all these problems are, we realise how active the solar plexus life continues to be.

In the mass of humanity the energy from this chakra is combined with the energy of the sacral and base chakras. In other words, our desires are often related to our appetites for sex, comfort and money. The positive attribute we call sympathy expresses itself through this chakra but is often combined with attachment to other people in a possessive way. Many family relationships are based on a possessive type of love which is expressed through the solar plexus. Who has not felt discomfort in this region from concern over the health or well-being of a loved one? Much of modern psychological practice is designed to remove the blocks of the solar plexus and to work on our emotions.

People learn to deal with these strong energies of the solar plexus through individual and group therapy. They want to be free of negative emotions and to acknowledge their feelings and desires. Apart from trained psychologists and psychiatrists, New Age teachers often conduct short workshops to help people feel positive and creative about themselves. You may perceive that many of these New Age gurus are dominated by their sacral and solar plexus consciousness which means they seek power and financial gain instead of having an altruistic motive. This is not to say that people who attend these workshops do not benefit from their adventures but others are left stranded when the guru leaves town.

As we grow and develop, the heart chakra opens and provides a more universal and unconditional love. We can see much evidence in the world of heart unfoldment through the many hundreds and thousands of individuals and groups who serve the planet in many ways.[5] Before the Second World War there were relatively few groups such as the Salvation Army, St Vincent de Paul and the Red Cross who provided service to those in need. The stimulation of the heart chakra enables the more self-centred love of the solar plexus and personality to be drawn upwards. This process gives us gradual control of an unruly solar plexus which for most people is thrown into motion with every passing astral current or desire.

Problems with under- or overstimulation of the heart chakra can promote various circulatory problems and lead to coronary artery disease which causes heart attacks. Lungs and breasts are also conditioned by the heart chakra. I have observed that many of my breast cancer patients have had a psychological trauma over 'heart' concerns. Possibly the great increase in heart disease, lung and breast cancer at this time in our planetary history is related to blocks of the heart chakra as our consciousness begins to focus through that centre.

Just as there needs to be a balance between the sacral and throat centres, a balance is gradually created between the solar plexus and the heart. Wisdom and understanding are two outstanding qualities of heart consciousness which relate to the buddhic or fourth plane, the central of the seven planes of consciousness. We see the heart as focussed through the middle point; the central plane in the larger cosmic scheme; the central energy flow called Force Flow 3; and sited in the central part of the body near the diaphragm. In an esoteric sense, the heart is considered to be a 'magnetic' organ meaning that it has drawing power and radiates inclusive love. Appropriately, it is found linked with what Fran Nixon called the magnetic force flow.

THE BASE CHAKRA

The base centre and the associated glands, the adrenals, are also linked with Force Flow 3. This relationship is understandable insofar as certain iron pigments are found in the adrenal glands, together with large amounts of vitamin C. The frequencies of iron and vitamin C are emitted by Force Flow 3. The frequency for sodium on this force flow has been mentioned in connection with digestion. Sodium is also involved with water balance and one of the functions of the adrenal hormones (hydrocorticoids) is fluid balance in the body. The adrenal glands also help us to survive in life-threatening situations and it seems appropriate that they should be connected with the force flow which is always present.

The base centre is related to the will to live and to be and it is no coincidence therefore that the adrenal glands react to stress and are involved with the fight and flight response. Hormones from both the medulla and cortex areas of the adrenal glands condition the sympathetic nervous system which is closely related to our astral body and to our emotional life. Thus any fearful or angry emotion causes adrenalin from the medulla or internal part of the adrenal gland to rush throughout the body. The adverse effect on our immune system of an adrenal response to constant stress has already been established by medical scientists.

The adrenal cortex secretes cortisone, sex hormones or androgens and other hormones which are associated with glucose and water balance. Cortisone is used to treat many life-threatening diseases which involve inflammation, swelling, or incompetence of the immune system which occurs in auto-immune disease. Conditions such as asthma, certain forms of arthritis, lupus, and ulcerative colitis are temporarily helped by cortisone treatment. Unfortunately, the administration of any supplementary hormones causes a further shut-down or suppression of that secretion in the body. In the case of cortisone, there are many side effects such as fluid retention, weight gain, and the masking of infections due to the suppression of the inflammatory response.

For all hormone medications there are natural remedies which can replace the need for hormone therapy in the long term, although it is obvious that it may be necessary in the short term to treat crisis conditions. There are also cases where it is necessary to prescribe hormones as a life-long medication. For instance, it is essential to give thyroxine if the thyroid gland has been removed. Fortunately, there are not many side effects from thyroxine which is used much less frequently than cortisone. It should be obvious to all of us that balancing our glands in a natural manner with remedies and techniques which have no side effects is the preferred approach.

The organs associated with the base chakra are the kidneys, ureters, bladder, and the spine. The external genitalia could be considered as being related to both the sacral and base centre. Health problems associated with this chakra involve all disorders of the adrenal glands, kidneys, bladder, and spine. These conditions will include nephritis, tumours of the kidneys, spinal problems, and cystitis. More subtle problems involving the energy flow through the base centre affect the basic level of our physical energy and our will to live and survive.

Both high and low blood pressure are related to imbalances in the flow of energy through the base centre. This is why the medical profession give beta-blockers to suppress the sympathetic nervous system in cases of high blood pressure. For long-term results, blood pressure can be treated by teaching people to meditate. This stimulates the part of our autonomic nervous system called the parasympathetic or the vagus nerve. In health, we have a balance between the two parts of the autonomic nervous system, the parasympathetic and the sympathetic. Our current 'busyness' tends to make our sympathetic nervous system dominant and this results in numerous stress-related disorders. This was first established by the well-known physiologist, Hans Seyle.[6]

An opposite condition produces low blood pressure. This occurs when insufficient energy is flowing through the base chakra. It is almost as if a person in this situation is not fully incarnated in the physical body. So in terms of base centre malfunctioning, there are two main problems. First, there are stressed people who are not able to relax and recharge themselves. Usually they don't find the time to do a physical activity (e.g. walking) that would enable them to tap the energy currents from the earth. Lifestyle issues such as wearing synthetic clothing, a poor diet and lack of sleep can affect energy transmission. Alternatively, some people have no energy flowing through their base chakra because they are just not focussed in their physical body. Young men and women who give the impression of being very vague and dreamy are examples of people who tend to be 'ungrounded'.

The base chakra is associated with the physical plane and, together with the sacral chakra, it involves focussing energy at the physical level. Both sacral and base chakras are associated with earthing and grounding. In a global sense, there is less to say about the base chakra. It will become active at a later stage in human development. At our present stage, the more negative aspects of the base chakra related to aggression are evident in, for example, terrorist activity. Thus we have the 'will to be' manifesting in a destructive way through groups who force their will on others. Eventually, the will for the good of the whole will manifest.

In a highly developed and spiritual person, the base chakra is linked with what is called the Kundalini energy and with the manifestation of spiritual will. This takes place when the base chakra relates to the crown after the latter draws up the energies from the base chakra through the unfoldment of spiritual attributes. A life of meditation and service to humanity or the other kingdoms in nature will be the precursor for this transformation of energy.

The techniques described in this book have a very profound effect on the base chakra because it has a powerful connection with the earth. To cope with strong energies we need to be earthed and many people today are not sufficiently grounded. Our lifestyle often tends to interfere with our link to the earth literally through the shoes we wear. Think of how many shoes we have with acrylic soles. Acrylic molecules block life-giving energy. Therefore if we habitually wear shoes with synthetic soles, earth energy cannot flow up through our feet and legs when we walk or run. Most jogging shoes have synthetic rather than rubber soles.

To properly ground ourselves, we need to be barefoot or to use shoes with soles made of natural substances such as leather or rubber. Both fashion and sport shoes can be found with appropriate materials if we take the time and energy to search. The more we support such manufacturers, the more likely they are to survive the synthetic explosion. Some synthetic materials are not as impervious to energy flows as acrylic and can be changed by exposure to the energy layers. Nylon and polyester are in this category and, although they cause static on the body, they can be inactivated by exposure to the energy layers.

People with chronic disease or long-standing exhaustion always have low energy in their base centre. Is it any wonder that our energies are low when we have no means of recharging ourselves because we prevent the healing energies from the earth from flowing through our feet!

The chakra corresponding with the base chakra is the crown centre which is situated just above the head. It is associated with the pineal gland. This gland is the conductor of the endocrine orchestra in many ways. It is concerned with two energy flows which we have not described as yet. We will explore these flows in the next chapter together with the other head chakras and their associated glands. These remaining chakras are the ajna, and its associated gland, the pituitary, and the alta major centre, and its mysterious gland which is sometimes called the carotid.

THE SPLEEN CENTRE

So far all the chakras discussed are psychic organs for different levels of consciousness. The spleen chakra deals purely with energy which is received directly from the sun in a physical sense and is not associated with any state of consciousness. It is the subtle counterpart of the spleen and is located in that position of the body – left of the midline and under the left ribs. I have found it to be partially blocked in cases of chronic fatigue syndrome. The spleen chakra functions best when there is some direct exposure of the central part of the body to the sun. This chakra and two other minor chakras on the torso form the pranic triangle.[7]

Although it is important to avoid excess sun it is also necessary to take a sensible position on the subject of sunbathing. The most appropriate time to sunbathe is when the sun is not near midday especially during summer months. We can use commonsense and receive the life-giving energies of the sun for short periods before ten and after two during the day. In winter, when sunlight is weak, the time is not a concern and we should take the opportunity whenever the temperature is warm enough, and situation suitable, for undressing. In tropical countries, precautions must always be taken against overexposure.

When we expose our pranic triangle to the sun, energy is circulated around it and distributed to all parts of the etheric body and then to the nervous system, organs and tissues. We also gain energy from the sun via the earth. This energy has already been processed by the earth and radiates outwards through the energy layers which are the central theme of this book. As there are parts of the planet which always receive energy directly from the sun, we can always receive some energy from the planet regardless of the local weather. However, just as there are blockages in the human energy body, there will be places on the planet where energy is received more easily than others. These are the planetary chakras, meridians and energy layers which may or may not be in a healthy state at any particular point in time.

In relation to energy flows, it is interesting to find that the spleen chakra registers on the 'white' flows which relate to the pineal gland and therefore to those hours with the most sunlight.

In summary of the ideas in this chapter, we have looked at most of the main energy centres or chakras which act as doorways into our body for all possible levels of consciousness. The chakras condition our etheric body or energy field, endocrine glands, meridians and receptors and indirectly, all physical organs and tissues. They are linked to the various energy layers on our planet. We will now look at the remaining chakras which are associated with the head and the white force flows.

9

THE WHITE FLOWS AND HEAD CHAKRAS

★ ★ ★ ★ ★ ★

WHITE has come to represent cleansing and purification. Throughout the ages religious groups have worn white clothing to symbolise purity. White is associated with spiritual light. In the science of colour mixing it occurs from a perfect blend of all colours. It is logical that the chakras associated with spiritual development will find their reflection on the 'white' layers. These chakras are the crown, ajna and alta major and they are all found in the head area.

Two substances traditionally associated with cleansing and enhanced immunity are associated with the white flows; garlic with the upper White Flow and chlorophyll with the lower White Flow. Garlic is found to contain selenium and germanium which both play significant roles in our immune system. The white flows carry the frequencies of many substances essential for life. It is now time to introduce these final two energy layers so that we can use them to correct and enhance energies in the body. The white layers and findings about the pineal gland featured in the last research done by Fran before she died at the age of seventy-five in 1985.

For the sake of continuity, we will first look at the main attributes of the head chakras and associated glands, and then undertake the adventure of charting the white flows.

THE AJNA CHAKRA AND THE PITUITARY GLAND

The ajna chakra is situated between the eyebrows and is connected with gathering up all the forces of the personality – this means the energies from all the chakras except those in the head. The ajna is related to the pituitary gland which secretes hormones that stimulate all the other endocrine glands. A feedback mechanism exists between the pituitary and the other glands so that a balance is maintained. A parallel situation exists between the ajna and the other chakras with the ajna expressing a synthesis of the whole personality life. At a certain stage of development, our energies are gathered up from all the other chakras and are focussed through this centre.

The feedback mechanism between the glands can be seen in the relationship between the pituitary and the ovary. It occurs when the ovarian secretion falls below a certain level. The anterior part of the pituitary then produces the follicular stimulating hormone (FSH) which causes more oestrogen to be produced from the ovary. The ovaries then take over and the pituitary secretion is reduced. At menopause, the ovaries can no longer respond and the pituitary produces larger amounts of FSH because there is no further input from the ovaries. Temporary side effects from this process are hot flushes, insomnia and general nervous upsets in many women. The contraceptive pill interferes with this natural feedback mechanism in childbearing women by suppressing ovulation through flooding the bloodstream with synthetic oestrogen and/or progesterone.

Other hormones from the anterior pituitary stimulate the thyroid, pancreas and adrenal glands. There is a delicate hormonal balance between all the glands. The nervous system is linked to the pituitary through an important structure in the head called the hypothalamus. This organ is situated near the pituitary gland and is intimately related to hormonal and nervous function.

Apart from the pituitary, the tissues associated with the ajna centre are the lower brain, left eye, sinuses and ears. Health problems arising from a disturbed ajna centre include migraine, sinus headaches, eye and ear trouble, and general nervousness caused by overstimulation of the nervous system. Brain tumours occur more rarely. Living at the point of tension may temporarily produce some of the problems mentioned here. As we develop an integrated personality life, the ajna centre awakens. People who have reached this stage are likely to become prominent figures or leaders in some sphere of life.

The more esoteric function of the ajna chakra is to receive spiritual impressions and ideas. These impressions are then worked into a pattern or plan by that level of consciousness which is expressed through the throat chakra. The ajna centre eventually becomes the distribution organ for spiritual energy that can be used for healing and other spiritual purposes. The centre can also formulate a spiritual intention from ideas received from divine levels of consciousness. Gradually the two head chakras, ajna and crown, establish an interplay of energies as we develop spiritually. This corresponds with a developing magnetic field which is established between the pituitary and the pineal glands. At this stage, the personality becomes the servant or transmitter of spiritual and soul energies.

THE PINEAL GLAND AND THE CROWN CHAKRA

The pineal gland is a small pine-shaped structure about 8 mm long ($1/3$ inch) which sits in the centre of the brain just behind the third ventricle. (There are four ventricles in the brain.) It is only recently that this gland has been subjected to extensive research. This apparent delay is in keeping with our tendency to make discoveries at a time which correlates with human and planetary unfoldment. There is more to say about this gland than the others because it has so much to do with our sensing and magnetic skills (see chapter 2).

The pineal gland has an indirect connection with our eyes and is related to both the nervous system and other endocrine glands. It is responsive to light through photo-receptor cells in the retina. This pathway along with stimulation from noradrenaline, a hormone transported by the sympathetic nervous system, results in the secretion of the pineal hormone melatonin. The pineal also secretes other hormones called serotonin and dopamine. It is associated with light in both a physical and spiritual sense. Perhaps there is significance in the fact that it also has the highest physical position in the body.

The history of the pineal gland is very interesting. From 300 BC to 1200 AD, leading thinkers believed that the pineal was a valve in the brain. In the 17th century the famous French philosopher, Descartes, spoke of it as the seat of the soul. Modern research began in the 1950s and established that this gland contains many minerals including calcium, magnesium, iron, phosphorus, zinc, copper and manganese. Other substances so far discovered include vitamin C, sulphur-based amino acids, glycerides, phospholipids, tryptophan and histidine.[1] Possibly the reason why this gland has the capacity to sense many frequencies is because it contains small amounts of numerous elements.

The production of melatonin which peaks between 2–4 a.m. each morning is responsible for the circadian or daily rhythms of the body. All the endocrine glands are interrelated but there is a particular relationship between the pineal and the gonads (ovaries and testicles). Secretion of melatonin tends to suppress ovarian function and thus it has been found that ovulation can be enhanced in infertile women if they sleep in a lighted room during their ovulation time. By so doing, they suppress the pineal secretion. This fact may account for why some women suffer menstrual irregularities when they travel long distances quickly and disturb their body rhythms.

Our body rhythms are disturbed following long air flights because the functioning of the pineal is interrupted and this contributes to jet lag. Melatonin tablets are now commercially available and are used by some travellers. The inhibition of the pineal hormone serotonin may also be related to inability to sleep after long flights because serotonin is related to the wake/sleep cycle. It appears that there may be a see-saw action between melatonin and serotonin secretion with the former peaking during the darkest hours of the twenty-four hour cycle, followed by a serotonin peak during the day.

The pineal gland exhibits a degree of calcification from the second decade of life onwards. From a medical point of view it is not known why this occurs. It has been speculated that the amount of calcification may depend on the level of serotonin secreted by the pineal. Fran Nixon was particularly concerned to discover ways of preventing and reversing the ageing or calcification of the pineal. She noted that when the energies associated with the pineal were strong, such persons had excellent memories and were inclined to be creative individuals. She also noted that they had an ability to resist levels of radiation which would seriously disturb the average person. These discoveries were made by testing the pineal wave responses of her students.

The magnetic sense in humans and its relation to the magnetic field of the earth is discussed in an article from the *International Journal of Neuroscience*.[2] The writer found strong indications that the pineal gland is a magneto-sensitive system, and that changes in the earth's magnetic field affect melatonin secretion and circadian rhythms. The strength of the magnetic field diminishes in winter.

This may account for the Seasonal Affective Disorder (SAD) which occurs in five per cent of the population and is usually attributed to light deficiency. The writer also suggested that the treatment for people with this disorder may be improved by applying magnetic fields as well as light therapy. Apparently the application of magnetic fields resembles acute exposure to light with respect to inhibiting melatonin secretion. Later in this chapter I will describe a method to stimulate the pineal gland by using the white flows.

This relation of the pineal gland to magnetic fields was anticipated by Fran Nixon's early discoveries. Robert Becker contributed by collecting the research done on the homing instinct of birds, animals and humans and its connection with our magnetic sense of direction. Remember, he described the minute crystals of magnetite embedded near the pineal gland which give us a homing instinct like that of pigeons. Fran's work on the Vivaxis energies, which relies in part on our homing instinct, pre-dates by many decades the magnetic sense described in the scientific literature.

We need to look at whether calcification of the pineal prevents sensitivity to magnetic currents. Do the people who suffer most when the magnetic field of the earth weakens during winter have significant calcification of the pineal? Do these people also have a loss of their sense direction? This finding would seem a logical explanation because calcification would surely diminish our capacity to respond to weak magnetic fields.

Recent research in an article entitled 'The Immuno-neuro-endocrine role of Melatonin'[3] reports that a tight physiological link between the pineal gland and the immune system is emerging from a series of experimental studies. Experiments which inhibit melatonin synthesis have induced a state of immuno-depression which is counteracted by administration of melatonin. A link between melatonin and the thymus gland has been established and we know that the thymus is intimately associated with immunity through the production of T-lymphocytes. This illustrates again the vital links between the various endocrine glands and the need for the balancing of their energies.

The crown chakra sits just above the head. This chakra is associated with the pineal gland. It forms a pair with the base chakra and is finally unfolded and vitalised in response to spiritual will. In a fully developed person, energies are drawn up the three spinal channels from the base centre by the unfoldment of the head, heart and throat centres. This happens in a natural sequence alongside the development of the higher or reflective mind (throat and ajna centres), the unconditional love of the heart centre, and the spiritual will which accompanies the unfoldment of the higher centres.[4]

At the planetary level it is not so easy to find a parallel to the unfoldment of the crown centre as we have for the other chakras. Humanity is not sufficiently developed in terms of spiritual will at this point of time. We are only just coming to truly understand the meaning of universal and unconditional love 2,000 years after it was first preached by Christ. Until this faculty of love/wisdom is fully unfolded, the will can often become destructive and dangerous and is best left to its slow development.

The tissues associated with the crown chakra, apart from the pineal gland, are the right eye and upper brain. Health problems directly related to the crown chakra involve disorders of the pineal including tumours, right eye problems and imbalances between the pineal and the pituitary. These imbalances can result in some types of migraines and in nervous problems. When a magnetic field is finally established between the pineal and the pituitary glands, a light around the head or halo is often seen by sensitive people. This stage of illumination indicates that the energies of the higher chakras above the diaphragm control the chakras below. It means that there is free passage for energy travelling up the three etheric spinal channels and it establishes a relationship between the three head centres. This brings us to a short discussion on the alta major centre which is a chakra less understood than the others.

THE ALTA MAJOR CENTRE

The alta major centre is situated behind the junction between the top of the spine and the base of the brain. It is therefore very close to the cerebellum or 'old brain' which is the more primitive part of the human brain. The associated gland is the carotid gland though it is rarely referred to in physiological texts. Students of meta-physical teachings have speculated that this gland may be the corpus cerulius, a small body which is found in the fourth ventricle of the brain situated very near to the brain stem. Recent research shows that nerve fibres connect the corpus cerulius to both the pineal and pituitary glands. This finding concurs with the esoteric concept that the three glands in the head and their associated chakras are all closely related.

The alta major centre, the lowest of the three head chakras, is the head chakra most related to the physical body. Energies flowing up the spine from all the other chakras pass through the throat chakra and alta major before passing into the head proper. This chakra is therefore also close to the throat chakra both anatomically and in some of its functions. It links up with minor chakras below the ears and is involved in conditions of vertigo or dizziness and also in cases of deafness. Other health problems may involve the cerebellum and brain stem. The precise function of the associated gland, the corpus cerulius, is unknown at this point.

Both the ajna and crown chakras register on the upper White Force Flow and the alta major is situated on the lower White Flow. The white flows are active between 10 a.m. and 2 p.m. At this point in time we are not aware of their full effect on the chakras. However, the health of our glands is enhanced by drinking water which is 'charged' on these layers between the times stated.

TECHNIQUES FOR FINDING THE UPPER AND LOWER WHITE FLOWS

Upper White

To locate the upper White Flow, you need the stimulation of light through your opened eyes. All the other force flows including the lower White Flow can be found with your eyes shut. Both pineal flows can only be found during peak daylight hours, that is, when the sun is near to its meridian, between 10 a.m. and 2 p.m. This force flow has a frequency which can be found by visualising either white or garlic.

Mark the other force flows first. Then stand with your arms and hands straight down with palms facing your sides and concentrate on white or garlic as you slowly tilt your head backwards from the position where your eyes are focussed on Force Flow 1. When the pineal receptor on the bridge of your nose is in line with the white flow on the ground, both your arms should pull towards the top of this force flow which is directly above the hand layer. In fact, once the hand band has been marked you will automatically know the position of the white layer.[5]

Lower White

With your eyes shut, arms at your sides, and hands with palms facing forwards, gradually tilt your head downwards below the phosphorus band while thinking of white or chlorophyll. When the pineal receptor on the bridge of the nose is in line with the lower White Flow, the arms pull forward towards the bottom of this force flow.

Now you have marked the complete set of life-giving energy layers from upper to lower white. During high and low tides, when Force Flows 1 and 4 disappear, the layers contract inwards and the force flows including the white flows will be found to have moved their positions until the solunar flow resumes. This is an important point to remember because some detrimental force flows are found not far from the white flows and these may move during the tides. They are less stable than the main energy layers and the lead force flow may come quite close to the normal position of the white flows during high and low tides. This is yet another reason to be precise with the timing of the exercises and to use the solunar flow times for most exercises.

THE PINEAL RECEPTORS AND THE WHITE FLOWS

An important pair of pineal receptors is located about 0.5 cm ($1/4$ inch) below the bridge of your nose. Other pineal receptors are spaced in a band around the head at that level including a pair on the back of the head, and also just above the auditory canal in each ear. In addition, there are pairs of pineal receptors on your body and, in each case, one of the pair will receive energy from the upper White Flow and one from the lower White Flow. Diagram 33 shows the position of the receptors associated with each force flow on the forehead and bridge of the nose.

Diagram 33

**RECEPTORS FOR THE VARIOUS FORCE FLOWS
ON CENTRE LINE OF FACE**

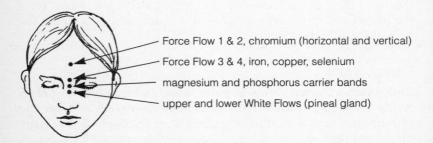

Force Flow 1 & 2, chromium (horizontal and vertical)

Force Flow 3 & 4, iron, copper, selenium

magnesium and phosphorus carrier bands

upper and lower White Flows (pineal gland)

These pineal pairs behave in the same way as the other receptors and swap their functions as you change your orientation towards your Vivaxis. As you respond to the upper White Flow with your eyes open and the lower White Flow with eyes shut, you can check how these receptors change their function by changing your position in relation to your Vivaxis. Use your testing finger while concentrating on white to find whether the pair is responding when your eyes are open or shut. If you move to the opposite direction in relation to your Vivaxis, the other receptor will then be activated. This means the recording hand will respond in one position with eyes open and in the other with eyes shut according to whether the receptor is responding to upper or lower white. As the receptors are positioned so close together there is no need to move the testing finger.

TESTING FOR CALCIFICATION IN THE PINEAL RECEPTORS

Start with the receptor pair on the bridge of your nose and confirm its position by concentrating on white while holding the point. There will be a response in your recording hand if you have found the correct position. To establish whether this pineal receptor is calcified, visualise chalk which is a form of calcium. If your receptor is calcified, a positive response in your recording hand will take place when you concentrate on chalk or calcium. The response in your recording hand may well be a circular motion which indicates disturbance.

I have reflected on the meaning of finding calcium in pineal receptors in some people. Calcium is one of the most important elements in the body but we know that it causes problems if it is found in the wrong places. Examples of calcification include kidney stones, hardened arteries, gall bladder stones, arthritic joints, and cataracts. We seem to have polarity between the pineal, the master gland of the endocrine glands which is linked to light, and calcium which signifies hardness, materiality and crystallisation.

However, there are a couple of paradoxes related to this view of calcium and the pineal gland. The first is that the body needs vitamin D in order to absorb calcium but vitamin D is manufactured by the skin through the influence of sunlight. The second paradox is that the pineal produces its hormone melatonin at the darkest time of the night. In weighing up the evidence it does seem apparent that the pineal should not be calcified for good health and spiritual

— 149 —

development. By using the energy from the white flows the effect of calcification in the pineal receptors seems to disappear.

Removing the Effects of Calcification in the Pineal Receptors

METHOD 1

Check the pineal receptors on your head by using your testing finger on the key receptors just below the bridge of the nose, above the auditory canals and on the corresponding level at the back of your head. Their position is established by visualising white and obtaining a response in your recording hand. If your recording hand responds when visualising calcium (chalk) in the pineal receptor, undertake the following steps between the hours of 10 a.m. and 2 p.m.

1 Check for normal ion in the environment and for solunar flow.

2 Fill a hot water bottle with very hot water – as hot as can be borne by the skin.

3 Roll or drag the bottle across all the energy bands on the ground from the lower White Flow upwards being careful to include upper White Flow but not beyond because of the detrimental flows some 10 cm (5 inches) above. Drag the bottle down and then up again each time including the White bands. Do not rest the bottle on the ground before treating your disturbed receptors as this will dissipate the energies in the water.

4 Hold the bottle against all disturbed receptors for a minute or so.

5 To balance with the other energies, exercise on all the energy bands except the whites and stimulate your memory receptors by singing a nursery rhyme.

6 Check your pineal receptors are now free of calcium by visualising calcium while touching the receptor with the testing finger. If there is no response in the recording hand, then the effect of calcification has been removed. Obviously, the gradual dissipation of the calcium may take days, weeks or months and therefore the receptors should be re-checked weekly over a period of several months.

METHOD 2

1 Check for normal ion in the environment and for solunar flow.

2 Stand on the lower white band. (We do not ever stand on the upper white band for any exercise.)

3 Using your middle fingers stress, alternately, the front and back pineal head receptors while facing your Vivaxis. Drop your hands and allow energy to flow in.

4 Stand sideways in your Vivaxis channel and repeat procedure with the pineal receptors located above the auditory canals.

5 Move to Force Flow 3 and stimulate your memory receptors by singing a nurse rhyme.

6 Exercise on all force flows from magnesium to phosphorus and then ground your hands on neutral ground after moving off the energy bands.

ENERGISING WATER WITH THE WHITE FLOWS

Prepare a jar of water by rolling it on all the force flows including the white flows between the hours of 10 a.m. and 2 p.m. The exercise must also be undertaken in the solunar flow time. Water that has been energised with the white flows holds the frequencies for many weeks. As the white flows have a purifying effect, perhaps the use of this technique is suitable in emergencies for purifying water.

It may be overstimulating to drink this water all the time. We need to undertake the earlier suggestions for testing food (and medications) by holding the food in one hand and testing for a disturbed response in the recording hand. Drink a few mouthfuls of the water whenever you obtain a positive response. Average needs would probably be every few days. On the other hand, our tap water has become quite adulterated with many added chemicals and bacteria are often present so that possibly it is advantageous to purify all our drinking and cooking water in this way. Each person must test their own situation and decide their needs.

Now that we have explored methods for restoring the most precious gland in the body to health, we will look at some practical ways of diagnosing problems within ourselves or others on the energy bands.

10

DIAGNOSING AND CORRECTING DISTURBANCES

* * * * * *

KEEPING a regular check on our health is a major benefit of working with the life-giving energy layers. It is a good idea to have these layers permanently marked on your property so you can inactivate food and clothing, as well as use them for your regular channelling of Vivaxis energies. If possible, the bands should be located conveniently close to the house to facilitate their everyday use especially during bad weather. However, the location will depend on the slope and position of your property.

For purposes of scanning yourself, it is also useful to have a band marked on a vertical surface such as a tree or wall. Be sure to use an unpainted wall and mark a position which is free of pipes and electrical conduits otherwise the energy layer may be distorted. The advantage of marking a band on a vertical surface is that it will only be 41 cm (16 inches) deep and we can then scan it very easily. Eyesight problems may reduce this option for some people if they experience difficulty focussing on narrow bands which are only 0.5 cm (1/4 inch) wide. In this case, the larger spread on a gentle slope is preferable. It is certainly desirable to become proficient at marking bands on both sloping ground and vertical surfaces. Sometimes you will be unable to find a patch of sloping ground and it is useful then to be able to mark the band on a wall.

Frequently people ask me about the effects of sleeping on a

particular layer, either a life-giving or detrimental layer. For instance, what happens if we sit or lie exactly on a lead band? There is no doubt that over-absorption of any particular frequency, even essential frequencies, can be unbalancing. But when we think about it, we do move around a lot, and we would need to be motionless a long time on an exactly level surface to remain only on the one energy layer. Even a mattress does not stay exactly level when we lie on it. My belief is that the discomfort we experience in certain chairs or positions is a natural warning to place ourselves elsewhere.

As we become more sensitive to energies, we find ourselves automatically choosing the right surroundings. A sensitive body apprehends disturbance easily and is aware immediately of discomfort or imbalance when contacting detrimental energies. Nonetheless there are times when we need to cope temporarily with a disturbance or pollution such as chemical, smog, or noise and we can then plan to move house or workplace and take the necessary steps to restore our balance.

RELATING NATURAL SUPPLEMENTS TO THE FORCE FLOWS

It is possible to ascertain the frequencies of a range of natural supplements and their location on the energy layers. I have found that all the vitamins register on Force Flow 3. Remember that this force flow is always present which is significant as vitamins are so essential for life. We can survive much longer without specific minerals than we can without vitamins as they are catalysts for many biochemical reactions.

I found the twelve tissue salts and the homeopathic range of remedies in low potencies ($12\times$ and lower) to be on the phosphorus carrier band. These are the dilutions which still contain some chemical molecules of the remedy. Many of the higher potencies such as the 30th centesimal and 200th centesimal register on the magnesium carrier band. These are the potencies which theoretically contain no physical molecules because they have been diluted so many times.

My findings illustrate that certain frequencies on the energy bands relate to the frequencies of homeopathic remedies. In addition, the higher potencies of these homeopathic frequencies correspond to the higher part of the energy band above chromium. For instance, a salt like iron phosphate is administered by homeopaths in a range of potencies both high and low. You will find that it registers on both carrier bands but its higher potency will register on the magnesium band and low potencies on the phosphorus band. Another commonly used remedy is arnica which is given for injuries. In low potencies it registers on the phosphorus band and again, the higher potency is found registering on the magnesium carrier band.

Since the frequencies and potencies of all natural remedies are found on the life-giving part of the energy layers it follows that regular channelling to the Vivaxis and exercising on the marked bands will provide the body with whatever frequency it needs. The regular drinking of water energised on the bands will likewise provide us with the vibrational frequencies needed. There is obviously a relationship between the frequencies of the energy layers and the subtle frequencies of homeopathic remedies.

PROTECTION FOR THERAPISTS

Not many practitioners will have immediate access to the energy layers at their place of work. However, as therapists, we have all had the experience of being drained or exhausted by certain patients. This process occurs when the patient, friend or relative drains energy from the energy field of the therapist in order to boost their own energy.

If a therapist is doing body work, especially if they hold bilateral points on the patient, (e.g. polarity therapy), a foreign field can be created. This creates a permanent link between the two people and causes severe energy depletion and, frequently, chaotic energy interference between the Vivaxis of each person. In other words, the individuals concerned no longer have a clear link to their own Vivaxis. A polarity therapist or a masseur could accumulate a number of foreign fields over a period of some years. This may be one reason why some therapists have what is called 'burn out'.

Several techniques can be used to alleviate or prevent these problems. First, the neutralising exercise described in chapter 1 should be performed after each consultation and especially after body work such as polarity therapy, massage, chiropractic, or kinesiology. The short version of neutralising is sufficient for about one minute. The connection made between the meridians of the finger tips and the strong circuit made by pressing ankles and knees together brings in our own energies and cancels out those of another person.

Regular channelling to your Vivaxis and drinking energised water are two processes which can strengthen your own energies when you have to work with a lot of people. You can keep a check on your ion flow and key brain receptors so as to establish the integrity of your energies.

In addition, if you are doing regular body work, it is a good idea to inactivate the treatment couch after each patient by going over it with the inactivator material as previously described for houses and cars. (see page 97). I also recommend inactivating the area over any electronic device used such as a Vegatest or Theratest machine. As with body work, therapists using electronic equipment should also do the quick version of the neutralising exercise after each patient. It is always possible to create a foreign field through holding an electrode which is connected with another person via electrical circuitry.

CHECKING YOUR HEALTH ON THE ENERGY LAYERS

All the life-giving elements on the energy layers should be present in your body and you should be able to assess your response to these elements by means of the energy flows present in your body.[1]

1 Make the usual check for solunar flow and check that your ion flow is balanced. Stand out of your four Vivaxis directions. Remember that the elements from Force Flow 1 and 4 will be missing at major and minor periods and also at new and full moon.

2 Stand back from the band and scan visually from the hand band downwards while thinking of yourself as if you are mirrored on the different layers. If the time is between 10 a.m. and 2 p.m. the white bands can be included.

3 Your recording hand should move back and forth or move in a wide sweeping motion while scanning yourself on all the force flows.

4 If you are investigating a particular mineral frequency, go to the layer which contains that element and visualise the element concerned while thinking of yourself. For example, to check your iron frequencies, go to Force Flow 3, visualise iron and then picture yourself on the level of Force Flow 3. Check for iodine on force Flow 4 and so on.

5 If an element is deficient your recording hand may not respond at all or, if there is a disturbance in the receptors involved with a particular element, your hand will move in a circular motion. For instance, if you smoke, your recording hand will move in this motion when visualising yourself on Force Flow 1 due to a disturbance of the oxygen receptors in your head. To differentiate between the different elements in this force flow visualise yourself in connection with the main elements one at a time – carbon, calcium, cobalt and oxygen.

The most important criterion in assessing the energy status of ourselves or others is the response in the recording hand. A zero response means literally that a person is not receiving the frequencies emitted by a particular force flow at that point in time. A circular motion indicates a disturbance on a force flow which can be itemised by visualising each element on that flow to find the problem. A healthy response is a strong back and forth motion as for normal ion flow or a wide sweeping motion.

People who have undergone a diagnostic or treatment procedure such as an electrocardiograph, X-ray, diathermy, ultrasound, encephalogram, CAT scan or nuclear magnetic resonance should check their ion flow or have it checked by another person and undertake the necessary clearing and energising procedures.

A few years ago, I did some interesting research with couples and watched their connection to the energy bands while they were giving each other hugs. In every case, as soon as the couple hugged it became impossible to monitor either person individually on the energy band. This occurs because a temporary circuit is formed between the two people which disconnects their individual circuits to their Vivaxis. It would be ridiculous to suggest that people should stop hugging but I wonder about the effect on the energy field of people who have intimate relationships with a number of partners. Does this create constant chaos in the energy field of such a person and is this a new argument for monogamy?

It could well be that we supplement the energies of each other at times and perhaps this replaces the need for our connection to the Vivaxis during short periods. What happens when two incompatible energy fields live and sleep in close proximity year after year? If one partner has a chaotic energy field does this always affect the field of the other? There are large areas of research yet to be undertaken.

CHECKING OTHER PEOPLE ON THE ENERGY LAYERS

One of the problems with any kind of sympathetic rapport with an unwell person is that you can pick up that condition yourself. Checking people indirectly via the energy layers protects us from being drained of energy or from acquiring the condition of the other person as can happen if we scan their body directly.

Follow the procedure for checking yourself except that you need to visualise the other person instead of yourself as you scan down the bands. There are certain times when you may be unable to detect any response from a person on any of the force flows. This usually occurs when the person is concentrating hard on some subject. So you need to check at another time when they are in a more relaxed state.

When a person is severely depressed I have found that they only register on Force Flow 1–3. I think depressed people have become so enclosed and cut off from the living world by their worry and introspection that they also cut themselves off from the life-giving flows of mother Earth. It seems amazing that some depressed people do not register on several energy bands for year after year and yet they survive. However, they are never missing off Force Flows 1–3, the central bands, except during major and minor periods when Force Flow 1 disappears.

Blood pressure drugs always cause the hand to move in a circular motion on the magnesium force flow when visualising the person concerned on that level. It may be that blood pressure problems are associated with disturbances of the magnesium receptors. You will recall that the magnesium receptors around the eyes are associated with the type of tension that causes short sight.

There are other magnesium receptors on the body. I thought that the magnesium receptors linked with blood pressure may be located in the area above the adrenal glands but to date have not found this to be so. Then I checked around the heart itself near the sternum and above the nipples on both sides of the body. The usual way to locate receptors is to visualise the element and then move the testing finger lightly around the chosen area until you record a response.

About 4 cm (2 inches) above the left nipple I found a magnesium receptor and on the corresponding point on the right side, a phosphorus receptor. The point on the left is very close to the heart. It is significant that there are minor chakras also found at these points above the nipple. It is amusing to speculate where these points will be if we have sagging breasts. Do the points correspond to the skeletal structure or to soft tissues? Obviously each person has to be individually assessed.

Magnesium is the mineral which relaxes structures in the body. Blood pressure is often due to tension and over-activity in the sympathetic part of the nervous system, which in turn causes arterial contraction and therefore an increase in blood pressure. Stress hormones are involved in this sympathetic nervous response. I have no doubt that other magnesium receptors exist and that they will be found to influence other organs and tissues. The need for adequate magnesium is a prime consideration in our stressed society.

Diabetes is a common disorder which I have checked on the force flows. Zinc and chromium are two minerals associated with blood sugar imbalance in diabetes. So far in my research in this area, the zinc receptors seem to be the most significant and this is illustrated by diabetics showing a disturbance on Force Flow 4. But they also have a disturbance on Force Flow 3 and this relates to the solar plexus which rules the function of the pancreas in an esoteric sense. This central chakra governs all the digestive organs.

In cases of dementia in the elderly, I have found that the recording hand registers a circular motion on all force flows. This circular movement also sometimes relates to spinal impediments which need chiropractic or similar adjustment. It is interesting to have a client with a known back problem and check them on the energy flows before doing body work to correct the misalignment. I have found that before the body work, my recording hand registers a disturbed circular motion on all force flows even if the problem is located at a particular spinal segment. But within minutes of the correction, a normal recording will be observed on all force flows. This is a very simple way for osteopaths, chiropractors and fascial therapists to check their work with clients.

Disturbances can also occur because pharmaceutical drugs have been taken for a long time. In these cases we will not only record disturbances on the main health-giving force flows but the person concerned will also register on the detrimental force flows (see later in this chapter).

SCANNING OTHERS DIRECTLY FOR DISTURBANCES AND IMBALANCES

Although it is preferable to teach people to assess their own energies, there are occasions when a therapist knows that a person has an energy block of some kind and that natural therapies are not working. In this situation we may not have access to the energy layers and may need to scan the person directly without the protection of the energy layers. Before starting any type of scanning, check for solunar flow time. Both the tester and subject should be standing out of their Vivaxis directions to prevent false readings.

Ion Flow

Ask the client to shut their eyes and count slowly to one hundred – this takes their mind away from you and the scanning process. Scan them back and front for ion flow. If your recording arm stops at some part, it usually means a complete lack of ion flow. In this case you should encourage the person to exercise on the energy bands after jarring the affected part, and then they should drink energised water. Ideally, the client should be trained to find their own Vivaxis so that they can 'channel' regularly, thus keeping themselves in a state of balanced energies.

It should be noted that there is usually a corresponding disturbance on the skull which accompanies any disturbance found on the body. The head should be carefully checked after finding a body disturbance. This area must then also be corrected, even if there is no sensation or problems noted by the individual concerned.

Foreign Fields

If you are testing a person for ion flow and your recording hand moves in a circular direction as you scan any spot on the body, you may have found a foreign field. Check this possibility by testing for a vertical flow. Hold the fingers of your recording hand in the vertical position (pointing skywards) while scanning that same place on the person. If your recording hand moves back and forth in this position you can conclude that there is a foreign field attached to that part of the body, given that there is both a chaotic horizontal wave and a vertical wave.

The most appropriate technique for removal of a foreign field is the long neutralising exercise. The affected person should repeat this exercise on at least three successive days. Make a check afterwards to ensure that the foreign field is eradicated. You should observe a normal ion flow on all parts of the body except on the exact midline. The person can then channel to their Vivaxis if they know how.

Scanning for X-rays

After a person has cleared themselves with carbon to erase the effects of X-rays, it may be useful for someone else to scan them for normal responses to the carbon frequencies, especially in the X-rayed areas. To do this ask the person to close their eyes and stand so that they are not facing any of the four quadrants of their Vivaxis, or directly into true north and south – the directions for carbon and calcium. The person then shuts their eyes and visualises carbon while the tester scans.

If their bones are responding correctly to the carbon/calcium frequencies, you should record a strong response in your recording hand from a carbon wave flowing throughout the body of the subject. If there is no response in your recording hand in some parts of the body, the subject has their carbon atoms in a state of imbalance and must do the clearing exercise for X-rays again.

Checking Brain Receptors

We can also test the important brain receptors of another person. I recently checked an elderly lady who had some form of dementia. The ion flow on her head appeared normal so I asked her to shut her eyes and perform a simple calculation while I checked all the main brain receptors. My recording hand moved in a circular motion when I scanned these positions.

Until this lady did some mental activity her head energies appeared normal in terms of ion flow. This particular lady had been in a home for the aged for fourteen years and had sat for long periods in her chair directly under a smoke detector throughout that period. The smoke detectors give out small amounts of radiation and if you stand under one for a few seconds, your recording hand will circulate wildly. It is possible that all her brain receptors had thus become disturbed. The same lady had also taken sedatives and tranquillisers for over thirty years. For protection from the radiation of smoke detectors you should avoid positioning a bed or chair directly underneath. The detectors can be installed in a part of the room that will not be occupied for long periods of time.

Steps for Testing the Brain Receptors of a Another Person

1 Your subject sits in a chair so that their head is entirely visible to you. They sit with legs apart and uncrossed and with a hand on each thigh. This is to stop the person forming a closed circuit which would obstruct the testing process.

2 Ask your subject to shut their eyes to keep out other influences and to hold their head tilted slightly to one side to avoid aligning to his/her Vivaxis. He or she then counts or multiplies while being tested.

3 The testing place must be on neutral ground and not directly under an electric light.

4 You, the tester, must also keep your head slightly off level and you must have all your own brain receptors in good working order, otherwise you may simply record a disturbance in your own receptors.

5 You then scan the subject's main brain receptors (see Diagram 25) and note the response in your recording hand. A circulating movement as usual denotes a disturbed receptor which can be treated by jarring it before the subject channels to their Vivaxis.

6 After scanning another person, you should do the neutralising exercise as soon as possible (the short one will do) to protect yourself from linking in with energy disturbances. Wherever possible people should be trained to do their own checking and scanning.

A CASE OF CHRONIC FATIGUE SYNDROME

Some years ago, I treated a young girl who turned out to be my first case of chronic fatigue syndrome although the medical syndrome had not been recognised at the time. The girl in question had developed pneumonia following bronchitis despite naturopathic treatment. After treatment with antibiotics she started to experience muscle pains and extreme weakness. Her mother had to carry her into my consulting room. I tried every imaginable therapy without a great deal of improvement.

In desperation, I explained the teachings of Fran Nixon to her mother and invited them both to my home for treatment on the force flows. On scanning her legs, I found that they had no ion flow from thighs to toes. As she was too weak to exercise on the energy flows, we carefully laid her on the ground in the position of the marked bands. The energy gradually returned to her legs and together with naturopathic treatment she made a complete recovery after some months. She is now finishing a university degree in biological sciences.

It is a sad thing that we tend to use the pure energy work as a last resort instead of in the first instance which is the more natural sequence. It was once the same with mainstream natural therapies. When I first went into practice twenty-five years ago, people came to us as a last resort. They had tried drugs and surgery and then with sick and broken bodies they were prepared to try vitamins, minerals and homeopathy. The same back-to-front process is now taking place with the more subtle therapies being requested after mainstream natural therapies have failed. Eventually, we will work in the right sequence.

When the subtle currents of etheric energy are disturbed in the body the logical process is to attend to the etheric body and then to give the vitamins, minerals and herbs to sustain the energy body. At the moment people are taking far more vitamins and minerals than they need, probably because the energy receptors for these substances are disturbed. However, natural remedies are certainly superior to drugs for most health disturbances because they have no side-effects of note.

DETRIMENTAL FORCE FLOWS

As well as monitoring the balance of life-giving energies in our bodies, we need to check for the presence of harmful substances. There are a number of man-made force flows which carry frequencies from insecticides, fungicides and drugs that are are detrimental to our health. There are also naturally-occurring force flows which carry elements such as mercury, lead, cadmium and aluminium. All these substances are toxic to the body and may be absorbed through the water we drink, the air we breathe or via the foodchain. Inner city dwellers are often exposed to high levels of lead from car fumes and most of us have been exposed to mercury from the gradual breakdown of amalgam fillings in our teeth and other sources. Many water reticulation systems use aluminium and chlorine in the purification processes.

While detrimental force flows should be generally avoided, we can use them as a touchstone to ascertain whether we have absorbed toxic frequencies. These force flows are found above and below the main band. Interestingly, the arrangement and position of the life-giving flows remains constant in different geographical locations but the distance between and arrangement of the detrimental flows varies from place to place. Usually the lead band is just about 10–12 cm (4–5 inches) above and below the white flows. This is why we need to be cautious and accurate in the process of rolling a water bottle on the bands to energise the water.

Most of the frequencies detrimental to life are beneath the main life-giving energy layers. A common arrangement starting below the lower White Flow is lead, cadmium, mercury, electromagnetic waves, insecticides, ionising radiation and aluminium. These will be spread over about 38 cm (15 inches) on a vertical surface below the main band. Lead is also found above the band.[2] See Diagram 34.

Finding the Detrimental Force Flows

The method you use now is exactly the same as you have used for finding the life-giving energy layers (see chapter 4). First visualise the element concerned and scan the area above and below the main band while tilting your head and with your eyes open. The vibrations from these elements are taken into the system while scanning, so limit the time taken to perform this exercise. Mark positions above and below the band as before.

To test whether you have these elements in your body, focus on the position of one of the toxic elements. Do not stand on any of the detrimental force flows. For the purpose of scanning the detrimental flows it is useful to have the energy layers marked as bands on a vertical surface. Stand back and visualise yourself on the position marked for that element on the ground or vertical surface and note whether there is a positive response in the recording hand. For example, find the lead band, and then mirror yourself on that band to see if your recording hand responds.

You can scan other people on these detrimental flows in the same manner. If someone has been on medical drugs for a long time you will also find that they will register on areas below the main band near detrimental elements depending on the drug concerned. To find the exact position of any prescribed drug, hold a sample in one hand and scan down below the main force flows until your recording hand responds. Visualise the person who takes this drug at the place you have marked and if a response occurs in

Diagram 34

POSITION OF DETRIMENTAL FORCE FLOWS ABOVE
AND BELOW LIFE-GIVING ENERGY LAYERS

lead
life-giving energy layers
lead
cadmium
mercury
electromagnetic waves
insecticides
ionising radiation
aluminium

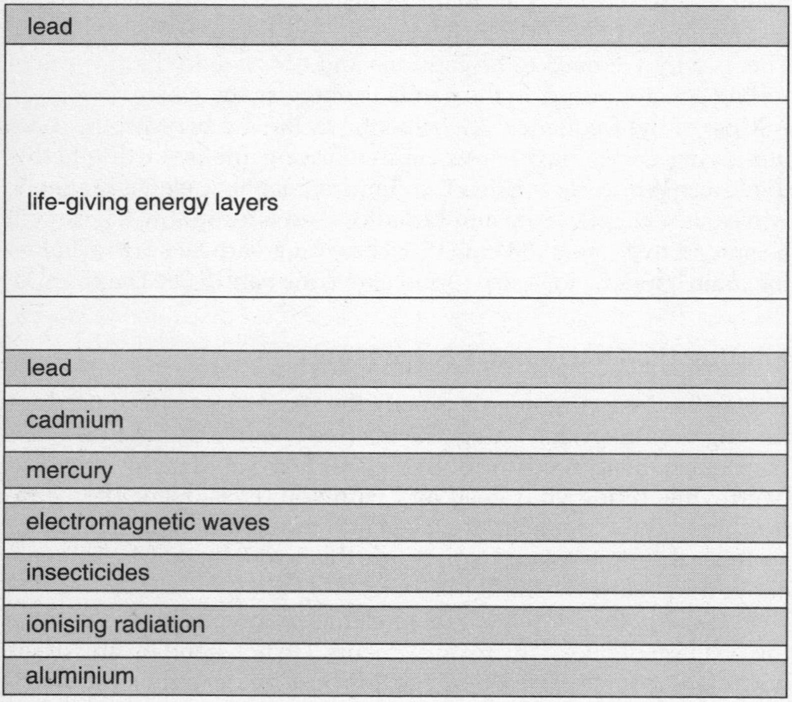

The positions of the detrimental flows may vary in different locations.

your recording hand, you can assume the person is adversely affected by the drug in question. Of course there will be situations where a person must take drugs for serious life-threatening diseases. The type of energy evaluation we do here merely indicates why so many drugs have side-effects, and also the importance of finding natural remedies wherever possible.

To help to neutralise the toxic substances associated with the detrimental force flows, drink water which has been energised by all the main force flows between and including the white flows and exercise on all the force flows from magnesium to phosphorus.

Channel to your Vivaxis on a regular basis. This regime will neutralise any negative effects from these elements and will also create resistance in your body to the over-absorption of negative frequencies.

CREATING A NEW VIVAXIS

The benefits of correcting energy imbalances are greatly diminished if a person has a foreign energy field. The only permanent solution for people who have established many foreign energy fields is to create a new Vivaxis. This means they will have a new permanent link to the energy field of the earth which will automatically cancel out other disturbed fields. This is not something to be done lightly for I think that there must be a reason why our Vivaxis is situated in a particular area. The soul coming into incarnation may well choose to have the Vivaxis at a particular place for reasons which we cannot understand. However, there are times when the creation of a new Vivaxis appears to be the best therapy.[3]

1 Select a place preferably hundreds of metres or yards away from any electrical installations. Try to take into consideration the possibility of future technology in the area. It is also best to be some distance away from large trees which may attract a lightning strike during a storm. Test the area carefully for ion flow and look for underground disturbances such as watercourses, and electrical cables. Near the bottom of a peaceful private garden is often the quietest and safest place.

2 Check that you are in a solunar flow period.

3 Find an energy band and mark all the force flows.

4 Exercise on all the bands from magnesium to phosphorus to strengthen your energies before you create a new Vivaxis and to minimise the old chaotic energies.

5 Stand on Force Flow 1 and turn slowly anti-clockwise in the Southern Hemisphere and clockwise if in the Northern Hemisphere while concentrating on chromium oxide (the green powder obtainable from potters' suppliers) which gives the frequency for chromium. It is this step which creates your new Vivaxis. It makes a strong Vivaxis to locate it directly on this energy layer. The result of such a location gives a direct flow of energies from the energy layer to your Vivaxis. It has been found that our Vivaxis is always linked to the nearest energy layer.

6 Move away to ground lower than the Vivaxis so that another person can test the success of the procedure. The tester stands next to the Vivaxis and places their left hand face down over the Vivaxis. Their recording hand is held in the position for recording vertical waves (fingers curled with tips pointing upwards). A vertical wave should be flowing from where you stand below your Vivaxis to your new Vivaxis site. A horizontal wave should also be recorded at the Vivaxis site. If you move above your Vivaxis the vertical wave cannot be recorded by a person standing at the Vivaxis site.

Many years ago, a close relative had a very bad nervous and mental breakdown. Although he had no actual organic diseases, he chose to stay in bed for nine months, only rising to use the bathroom and to eat. At his own request he underwent many types of healing which included magnetic, colour and spiritual healing. I perceived that his energy field was a seething mass of chaotic energies and suggested that a new Vivaxis be made. We chose the quiet garden of a friend whose property had sufficient slope to mark the energy bands.

The new Vivaxis was established but my relative did not feel particularly enthusiastic, probably because he had believed for nine months that he would die very shortly. However, within a few days his outlook improved and within a few weeks he completely regained his health and interest in life. At the age of seventy-five this man is actively working in his chosen profession nearly twenty years after his breakdown.

Do consider the site you choose very carefully because different weather conditions affect the energies at the site. This fact was forcibly brought home to me after I helped a man with many health problems make a new Vivaxis. I selected a particular site but my client wanted another place. The site he chose was about one thousand metres from high tension overhead electrical cables. However, despite the considerable distance allowed between the power lines and this site, to be quite sure, I had chosen a site further away. At the time his choice seemed clear of disturbance and so we went on with the procedure after I had tested the ion flow and found it to be normal. The weather at the time was very misty with lots of water-vapour in the air.

A few weeks later, the man rang me in great agitation saying that he felt most disturbed and the disturbance seemed to be coming from his new Vivaxis. I immediately went out and found his site which I had clearly marked. The weather on this day was very clear. To my horror, I found that the Vivaxis site was now affected by the electromagnetic field coming from the power lines. I realised that the misty weather at the time of the procedure had broken down the electromagnetic field closer to the power lines and that in clear weather the field extended much further.

We arranged to destroy this Vivaxis at a particular time and the man was advised to find another suitable location on which to stand as I destroyed the unsatisfactory Vivaxis by passing the in-activator material over the site. The moment that we cancel out our Vivaxis, a new one will automatically form in connection with the force flow nearest to the person concerned. As the area of the Vivaxis I destroyed was higher than his present location I was able to test that the Vivaxis had been destroyed by confirming that the vertical wave had disappeared. This meant that his new Vivaxis had formed.

This experience taught me two important points. First, to check a proposed site more than once and preferably in different weather conditions several days before making a new Vivaxis. Second, that it is better not allow another person to override my own intuition about how the exercise should be done.

It only takes a few moments each day to check our energy fields and to do strengthening energy work. We are now in a position to monitor the energy flows and mineral status of ourselves and others. We have also discussed how the energy layers reflect the frequencies of minerals, herbs and homeopathic remedies used to restore health and balance. Observations of the detrimental force flows should enable us to monitor any build-up of toxic waste which could threaten life and health. In addition, when needed, we can create a new Vivaxis.

11

EARTH PHENOMENA WHICH AFFECT OUR LIVES

★ ★ ★ ★ ★ ★

*I*N THE human body there are minor and major energy pathways which we usually refer to as meridians. Planet Earth also appears to have minor and major lines of energy. These 'tracks' are called ley lines. Throughout history, temples and cathedrals have been built over power spots which often coincide with an intersection of ley lines (see Diagram 35). These energies appear to enhance the effect of meditation and the old master builders were taught how to find the right sites for sacred buildings, cathedrals and sometimes small churches. Many of these builders belonged to secret guilds associated with the Rosicrucians and masonic teachers who gave spiritual training in the use of subtle energies to their members.

LEY LINES

The concept of long straight tracks of energy connecting sacred and meaningful sites was revived this century by Alfred Watkins. He was born in Hereford, Britain, in 1855 and was a county councillor and magistrate, and a miller of flour by trade. He took a great interest in the countryside and noted how various hilltops appeared to connect sites of interest. Initially, he thought these may be ancient traders' tracks. Later, using ordnance maps he found a

Diagram 35

LEY LINES CROSSING UNDER CENTRE OF GREEK TEMPLE

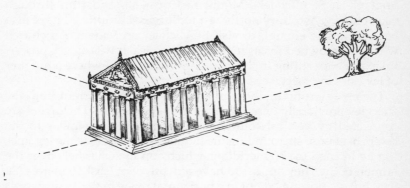

number of cases where four and five churches could be connected in a straight line.[1] The Straight Track Club was formed in the United Kingdom by Watkins in 1926.

Interest in ley lines has been maintained during the intervening decades. Paul Devereaux is a leading researcher in the area who together with Andrew York conducted a project to establish whether there are connections between sacred sites, geological faults, meteorological events and UFO sightings. Every stone circle in England and Wales was found to be within one mile of a surface fault. Devereaux also investigated the phenomenon of earth lights in these areas. These are mysterious lights which have been reported by a number of people in the area of sacred sites. The lights often dance around the site, appearing and disappearing at random.

A further investigation, the Dragon project, looked at ultrasonic pulsings which are emitted from some stones in sacred sites. The Rollright stones in the Cotswold area of England were chosen for this project. This particular site is rich in folklore. Pulsings from some of the stones were found to occur during winter before sunrise at the new and full moons.[2]

During my travels through Europe, I examined many sacred sites and found that ley lines are usually running down the longitudinal axis of sacred buildings. In Greece, I checked several temples and found that this was also the case. In some special temples such as the Parthenon on the Acropolis in Athens, there is an intersection of ley lines in the middle of the building.

In the south of England, I examined the ley line running over the well-known hill, the Tor, at Glastonbury on which lie the ruins of a church called St Michael. This section of the Michael ley line enters England at St Michael's Mount in Cornwall, and runs through Glastonbury, Avesbury north-east to Bury St Edmunds. I have also been fortunate enough to visit St Michael up Marsden, a church which is renowned for its incredible energies. It was a very powerful experience sitting in this church which is sited where a number of ley lines intersect.

The energy running through ley lines is quite different from the energies previously described in the energy layers. The layers are connected by vertical columns of energy and are similar to the layers of energy surrounding the human body whereas the ley lines can be likened to the meridians which run like channels over the human body. They appear to have a depth of at least 10 metres (30 feet) but are not spread out in a horizontal plane in the same way as the energy layers. The energy flow in the lines reverses at the new and full moons. The energy in these earth meridians is stronger than our own energies and it is impossible to test for ion flow while standing in a ley line. In fact it was an absence of normal ion flow on a section of my property which first led me to discover a ley line.

In ancient times it is possible that people understood how to work with earth energies by holding rituals at sacred places situated on ley lines. We can think of these sites as acupuncture points on the surface of the earth meridians and perhaps through ceremonies and beacon fires, the energy was distributed from one meridian to another. The standing stones are like acupuncture needles placed in special points on the ley lines to transmit energy. It is also possible that ancient cultures had some kind of telepathic communication through ritual from one site to another via the ley-line system.

While these energies are suitable for spiritual purposes, it is not wise to live on top of them. I discovered this for myself when I lived in a house east of Melbourne directly on a ley line. Despite the experience being very challenging, it enabled me to understand these energies intimately during the ten years of my residence at that place. It was by chance that I made the discovery and it may make interesting reading to describe the event.

Discovery of a Ley Line

We had been resident for several years and many people mentioned that they felt the house was in a special place. I frequently held meditation gatherings for various purposes and the house was surrounded by several acres of bush in a quiet street in Ringwood, a Melbourne suburb. With its sloping grounds, the property was eminently suitable for teaching Vivaxis. I had carefully checked that the site was a sufficient distance from nearby high tension power lines by testing for ion flow on the side of the property nearest the lines. However, I had not checked every part of the property for normal energy flow due to its large size of around five acres.

About six years later, during the mid-eighties, we were disturbed by a strange repetitive sound during the night for some weeks. It sounded like electronic beeping and was very penetrating. We checked the various electrical appliances in the house and pondered on the origin of this disturbing sound. I was becoming exhausted from lack of sleep.

One night at about 4 a.m., I went outside in an effort to trace the sound. I moved towards the noise and began testing ion flow on the ground to see if there was anything unusual. As I drew near to the sound which seemed to be coming from a large eucalyptus tree, the ion flow cut out. Suddenly, there was a movement in the tree and an enormous black bird flew out. I had never seen such a bird before. It was pitch-black and larger than a crow. The noise near the tree appeared to be coming from the bird.

So I had solved the mystery of the noise, but was now fascinated to find that this tree was the centre point of a very strange energy phenomenon. It was almost as if the bird had called and led me to the place. In daylight I investigated these strange energies and found that the tree was at the intersection of a line which went straight through the house and beyond for as far as I could test. Another line was at right angles and also went as far as I could test. I found these lines by looking for areas where normal ion flows did not register and then I switched my focus to sense the type of energy in the line. It was a strong energy which pulled my hands and body along in the direction of the line which was about three metres or yards wide. It travelled through the house and just cleared my bed for which I was thankful.

I wondered why I had not noticed this energy line at an earlier time. It is interesting how we can miss a phenomenon until we are actually confronted with something out of the ordinary. When we focus on a particular area, we tend to notice only general effects or whatever we are expecting and this accounts for the tremendous bias we can develop especially in our home surroundings. We need to check and recheck our findings whenever we come across a new manifestation of energy but we should not ignore our results just because they do not fit into our existing model. Unfortunately, some people attracted to working with energies are too astrally-focussed and hence do not use their discrimination. Sloppy research does a great disfavour to those investigators who are thorough.

THE TYPE OF ENERGY IN A LEY LINE

The energy at the site of the tree in the example above was spiral in nature. If I stood at the intersection of lines near the tree and relaxed, my whole body started to gyrate in a slow circular fashion from the feet upwards. In later months I found that the direction of the spiral reversed at each new and full moon and this coincided with a change in direction of the flow within the lines.

One line was running north to south and the other east to west. I found that at the full moon the lines expanded considerably and took up nearly the whole house in width. This made it very difficult to sleep because my bed was within the energy flow. It gave me a feeling of restlessness in my legs although I found it was a positive force when meditating. I began to understand why places of worship and sacred buildings were located on these sites but not residential dwellings.

Another interesting phenomenon was observed by my co-worker from Canberra when she came to stay and assist me with healing seminars. She had trouble going to sleep due to the extra energy rushing through the house. She also suffered from the restless limb problem and compared her night's sleep to lying on a walking track with disembodied entities wandering through each night. This was an aspect I had not considered but it seemed logical that a ley line could have a psychic dimension which carried a lot of 'traffic.' Later I read in a most interesting book about earth mysteries by Phillip Heselton that ley lines are traditionally paths of psychic activity and lines of a seasonal flow of spirit.[3]

I decided to have the position of my ley lines confirmed by Alanna Moore who was experienced in working with subtle energies including map dowsing. She was living hundreds of miles away in New South Wales but confirmed my own evaluation by sending back a street map marked with the lines and made some interesting suggestions about how to deflect the energy if necessary. Alanna is experienced in many kinds of earth phenomena and I am indebted to her for supplying some of the research about the geopathic stress described in the next chapter.

As I became more familiar with the characteristics of the terrain and vegetation on ley lines, I noticed that a tree with unusual formation often grows at an intersection of lines. The tree outside my house at Ringwood had two trunks which were twisted in a strange formation not typical of the eucalypt species. I reasoned that the energies of the two lines had contributed to this double trunk and the spiral formation.

Perhaps we are attracted to unusual home sites because of an interest in subtle energies but I found it increasingly difficult to live in the Ringwood house. Continual changes in the etheric body of the earth caused the ley line to become wider each year. So, as there were other reasons to sell the house, I decided to move into a small cottage near the top of Mt Dandenong. After my recent experience, I carefully checked the house and it seemed quite free of unusual energies and I moved in.

After a few weeks I began to muse about the enormous eucalypt near the front gate. This tree is now over 30 metres (100 feet) tall and has no less than five huge trunks. I wondered if it was on a ley line and soon found that it has grown directly on the powerful line which runs from Mt Dandenong to Melbourne. At least this line does not go through the house – even with its expansion at the full moon it is at least 20 metres (60 feet) away. This find has allowed me again to monitor a ley line at close quarters and to confirm the reversal of the energy flow at new and full moon. On my walks in the nearby forest, I have found another intersection of lines which is also marked by a eucalypt with five trunks.

It is not necessarily the case that all such intersections will be marked by a multi-trunked tree but there is usually some significator. Some years ago, a friend with a fifty-acre property asked me to see if I could find a ley line. On this occasion I started out on foot and allowed my instinct to carry me to a particular area. In this area, I noted a very large, white-trunked eucalypt and began detailed checking. Sure enough, this tree was marking the intersection of two energy lines. One line led to a magnificent spring which fed a sizeable lake providing water for the surrounding farms. It is not uncommon to find springs in the vicinity of ley lines.

In Australia, we are not aware of ancient buildings or sacred sites on ley lines as in Europe and Asia. Many ancient sites are secret to different groups of Aboriginals. Over time, some of the knowledge of these very sensitive and psychic people may have been lost but there are indications in Dreamtime stories that ley lines were used. Because sacred sites in Australia are not marked with architectural features, we must note more natural signs as manifested by rocks, trees and contours of land to give us clues.

FINDING A LEY LINE

You will need to search in an area that is not built up with typical small suburban blocks. A National Park is a suitable place for finding a ley line. Establish the general area by means of the type of observations mentioned or by any more subtle sense of intuitive knowing. If the opportunity presents, I recommend that you first start this type of sensing at a large cathedral or temple which is some centuries old, and therefore likely to have been sited by a master builder.

1 Scan across either end and each side of the building to find the direction where normal ion flow is not present. Mark where ion flow begins and ends.

2 Stand in the middle of the flow and allow your body to register the direction of the energy flowing in the ley line. The line will probably be on the longitudinal axis of the building. If possible, revisit the site after the next new or full moon and recheck the direction of the flow.

3 Some people feel comfortable locating ley lines with dowsing rods. If you prefer this method, hold the rods in front of your body so that they are in a parallel position as you approach the building. Think 'ley line' as you approach and note the position where the rods swing outwards. As you dowse for water, the same movement will occur when you reach the edge of the watercourse (see Diagram 36).

4 Turn at right angles so that you face into the flow or have your back to it depending on the direction of the flow. The tips of the rods will swing in the direction of the flow and remain parallel. As you move along with the flow, the tips will turn to follow the direction of the ley line. Diagram 36 indicates how the rods swing outwards when we approach the edge of a ley line. A very useful book published recently called *The Dowsing Handbook* has contributions from many authors and includes a kit containing copper rods.[4]

I prefer to use my arms, hands and body rather than the rods, but the rods are easier to use if you are charting a ley line over a long

Diagram 36

DOWSING A WATERCOURSE

When you reach the watercourse the rods swing outwards.

distance in a moving car. Only an experienced dowser could undertake such a task but it was successfully managed by Hamish Miller
and Paul Broadhurst for the purpose of charting the famous St
Michael line across southern England.[5]

The dowser has to be quietly concentrating on the energy line in
question as there are many side lines which feed in to the ley
line being followed. By concentrating intensely on the task, we
automatically block out other phenomena such as watercourses,
electrical cables and water pipes which could affect our accuracy.
If you dowse without giving the task your full attention you may
pick up a number of energy factors but you will not know what
they represent.

Once you have practised finding ley lines on a known ancient
site, and you are feeling confident, move into a country area and
start to look and sense for signs connected with trees and rocks.
Sometimes you will find them in the least expected places. I was
touring with friends in north-east Greece and we stopped for the
night at a small hotel near the sea. I was gazing out from my
balcony across the small backyard when I saw a strange yellow

stone standing by itself. It had the usual shape of a standing stone although there was nothing else of significance in sight.

I could detect there was no normal ion flow associated with the stone and sure enough with further checking I found it was situated on a ley line. The stone had probably been placed there a long time ago by someone to mark the line. The present owners would have been quite oblivious of the fact but may have been attracted by the special energy which would have been apparent to a sensitive person. Perhaps we should have asked about this possibility.

LEY LINES, EXTRATERRESTRIALS AND ATOMIC DETONATIONS

The work of Bruce Cathie, a retired airline captain from New Zealand, sheds light on the existence of ley lines. Cathie is the author of a number of books on ley lines which he describes as the energy grid of the earth. During his work as an airline captain over several decades, he had sightings of various unidentified flying objects (UFOs) and he started to tabulate these sightings and those of others in terms of the ley line or grid system. He spent many years perfecting the mathematics of the grid system and is now selling a software programme which can display the grid in any part of the world.

Of particular note is his finding that UFOs appear to land on strategic points of the grid system. In fact he suggests that these space craft may use the energy in the grid system as fuel. Cathie has investigated hundreds of sightings and mapped their locations to establish his hypothesis. In some instances, these craft have been observed hovering over a grid line for extended periods of time.[6]

Even more spectacular was Cathie's discovery that the detonation of atomic bombs always takes place over a grid line and at the time of a particular astronomical arrangement. He monitored the positions of many test sites and the detonation times to verify this fact. The main grid has been established by Cathie to be roughly in a geometric arrangement of square miles so it is obviously not difficult to establish a suitable site for atomic testing. While the general public has known nothing about this grid system it seems likely that some military centres have known and used the grid for many years.

We are considering therefore an energy pattern over the entire earth which is just as intricate as the many major and minor meridians of the human body. The siting of ancient monuments in both the East and West indicate that the ancients also knew about the planetary ley lines or grid system. Cathie is the first person to map this system in a detailed mathematical way and to present it to the general public.

Some of the famous ley lines that connect ancient sacred sites will be man-made, arising from the many pilgrimages and holy treks which have been made over the centuries. These auxiliary lines may be connected to the natural grid lines at particular points thus establishing a most intricate system.

Although we do not have much information about Australian Aboriginal sacred sites, they are probably also connected to the ley lines. For ten years I was joint owner of a twenty-acre property at Kinglake which is situated 600 metres (2,000 feet) above sea level in bushland on the Great Dividing Range. It was here that the first Vivaxis seminar took place in 1980 and therefore I was very conscious of experimenting with earth energies on this property.

Some metres below the house in a small basin was a natural ellipse formed by a number of large eucalypt trees. A central tree on this ellipse had a most interesting spiral trunk marking the position of powerful earth energies connected to the ley line system. The trees marking this oval shape were connected by a flow of unusual energies. So often discoveries about earth energies are made by chance. We notice where normal energies cut out, and then go about exploring the different energies. This seems to me a more healthy way of working than looking always for the peculiar. By focussing on the normal, perhaps one is protected from becoming peculiar.

One end of the ellipse coincided with an underground spring. A number of acquaintances who visited the site felt that it contained powerful energies. One woman who has lived with Aboriginal people thought it likely that this area was used for religious purposes. I used to meditate next to the spiral tree on a huge stump which was part of the ellipse and I found it to be a very special place.

To summarise the significance of these energy lines, we can say that the earth is covered by a grid which probably has the purpose of distributing energy from one place to another and thus nourishing the earth with the energy or prana received from the sun. Due to the relationship of the earth with other celestial bodies, the energies in the grid fluctuate from day to day and week to week. Humans versed in the ancient wisdom have always known how to find this grid and to use it for both sacred and sometimes profane purposes. Master builders have raised edifices and structures to concentrate and distribute the energy and this is why many cathedrals, churches and temples are found on ley lines and on the intersection of ley lines.

It appears that extraterrestrials also know about the grid system and their inter-planetary travel may well rely on the recharging of their craft from the grid system. It also is apparent that the release of energy from the atom by fission relies on a knowledge of the grid system.

RELATING THE DIFFERENT TYPES OF EARTH ENERGIES

Let us reflect on how ley lines and the energy layers are related to both the planet and the human body. By way of explanation we can compare the planet with the human constitution. In the body there are major energy centres called the chakras; minor centres with conduits called meridians that connect major and minor centres; and lesser channels again which are probably those chains of triple groups that Fran Nixon discovered running in lines on the body. All of these etheric manifestations form the interface between the human nervous system and those more subtle expressions which relate to our emotions, minds and spiritual being.

On the planet, we also have major channels called ley lines which criss-cross the surface of the earth forming minor and major power spots. The largest planetary centres are marked according to Alice Bailey's teachings, by cities such as London, New York, and Tokyo. These cities are said to arise through their magnetic attraction for humans over the centuries, this being the underlying cause for the more mundane activities of trade, commerce and position.[7] There are also minor centres which are often marked by sacred buildings.

In a horizontal plane, Fran Nixon discovered the fine planetary layers of energy which are like the skins of an onion surrounding and interpenetrating the planetary surface. These are similar to the energy layers she found in the human etheric body – the magnetic and gravitational layers of the aura. The sphere of energies which forms the connection between our personal energy layers and the planetary layers is of course the Vivaxis.

There are also other energy grids called the Hartmann and Curry grids named after discoverers (discussed in detail in chapter 12).These grids form a fine network throughout the planet and can be likened to the planetary nervous system. It is interesting that Nicola Tesla who discovered how to make the alternating current of electricity also discovered and demonstrated that electricity could be conducted over long distances without wires. Being far ahead of his time, he never received the support for that project or for other significant research programmes which involved anti-gravity devices based on an understanding of ether as anti-matter.[8]

A LIGHTNING VIVAXIS AND ITS TRANSFER THROUGH SPACE

Electrical activity on our planet is another earth phenomenon which produces amazing results. Earlier we described how there is a constant electrical potential of 400 volts per square metre. This is the measure of the electrical tension between the surface of the earth and the ionosphere which can probably be compared to the outer band of the etheric layers around the human body.

A build-up of positive ions in the atmosphere following hot, windy weather causes static and an imbalanced ion flow (ions being charged particles). This situation is balanced out in a thunderstorm with the discharge of electrical energy of some millions of volts in certain locations. Vertical structures such as steel towers and even trees attract such a discharge and we are advised to keep indoors during a storm. During an electrical storm, negative ions are produced and the balance between negative and positive ions is restored.

At the site of a lightning strike, Fran Nixon discovered a permanent Vivaxis of quite enormous proportions (see Diagram 37) and she undertook an intriguing experiment which can be repeated by anyone who finds a tree that has been struck by lightning. While staying with her in Canada, I witnessed and took part in the following experiment which involved the transfer of a lightning Vivaxis to another site through space using the Vivaxis connection. Fran devised this experiment to show how the energy from a large Vivaxis can be transferred through space. The following steps were undertaken.

1 During solunar flow period, a calcium tablet was placed in a paper cup over neutral ground. Several perforations were made in the bottom of the cup for drainage purposes.

2 A pinch of ascorbic acid was dissolved in half a cup of fresh seawater and then poured over the calcium tablet. The solution drained through the perforations and the tablet was allowed to dry. We were then able to record a small Vivaxis of about

Diagram 37

A VIVAXIS CREATED BY A LIGHTNING STRIKE

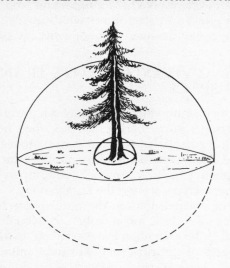

15 cm (6 inches) in diameter. The Vivaxis registered as a chaotic circulating motion in the recording arm in the 15 cm space around the tablet. A vertical wave was also recorded.

3 The calcium tablet was then transported to the site of the lightning strike 7 kilometres (4 miles) away whereupon we recorded that the Vivaxis energy at the first site had expanded to about 8 metres (25 feet) in diameter. Our energy fields felt disturbed and chaotic after only sixty seconds of contact with this enlarged Vivaxis. We were affected by blurred vision and were unable to record normal ion flow on our bodies.

4 The calcium tablet was then returned to its first site and it was found that it was now wave linked to two Vivaxes with a dividing line down its centre marking the connection to each Vivaxis. We can understand how disturbing it is if a person becomes linked to a foreign Vivaxis, especially a powerful one.

5 The tablet was then destroyed along with its disrupting Vivaxis.

Fran asked two clairvoyants to observe the two-way Vivaxis energy flow from the tablet to the site of the tree. They both drew the effects and did not compare notes until they had finished their observations. They described each stream of energy as 25 cm

(10 inches) wide with 10 cm or several inches separating the flows. The centre of each flow moved in rapid spiralling motions and radiated sparkling colours of vivid hues. They also described the huge energy field around the tree. Fran concluded from her researches that Vivaxis waves are responsible for transporting the energy of one Vivaxis to another.[9]

This extraordinary experiment does indicate to some extent the relationship between the electromagnetic phenomenon of our planet and the Vivaxis energies. It would be very interesting to know whether lightning is more likely to strike a point on ley line.

12

HARMFUL EARTH ENERGIES – GEOPATHIC STRESS

★ ★ ★ ★ ★ ★

WE HAVE looked at a number of beneficial energies flowing through planet Earth and some of the harmful energies in our planetary environment. There are many man-made problems from X-ray radiation to atomic fall-out which have already been accepted as potentially causing genetic effects on living things. In addition, there is a growing body of scientific evidence to indicate that people and animals can become ill and even die if exposed to some of the naturally-occurring phenomena called geopathic stress.

WHAT IS GEOPATHIC STRESS?

The term geopathic stress has been used increasingly to cover a wide range of both naturally-occurring and man-made problems which exist in our environment. Underground watercourses, rock fissures, energy knots from the intersections of the Hartmann and Curry grids, oil deposits, electromagnetic pollution from power stations, power lines, transformers, microwave ovens, microwave transmitters and dishes all cause energy disturbances.

Underground watercourses are the most common form of geopathic stress encountered in our environment. Considerable research has taken place in Russia, France and Germany on this subject in relation to cancer and other serious health problems. In some German educational institutions architectural students are taught building biology (Baubiologie) to help them design safe buildings avoiding harmful sites which could produce disease in future residents (see Diagram 38).

Before the Second World War, Pierre Cody, a French engineer demonstrated the link between ionising radiation and cancer in studies over a seven-year period. With the support of an eminent physicist, Louis le Prince-Ringuet, an Elster and Geitel electrometer was used to register disturbances under the beds of 7,000 cancer sufferers. These readings were compared with readings a few metres away and radiation levels were found to be ten times higher directly under the beds of the cancer patients. The radiation appeared to rise directly upwards, in some places through several floors, without any diffusion.[1]

In southern Germany during the 1930s, Baron Gustav von Pohl conducted the most famous evaluation of cancer sites through dowsing techniques. In conjunction with local authorities in the town of Vilsbiburg he accurately located the homes of fifty-four people who had died of cancer. Initially he mapped the detrimental sites in the whole town and then compared locations with the

Diagram 38

UNDERGROUND WATERCOURSES

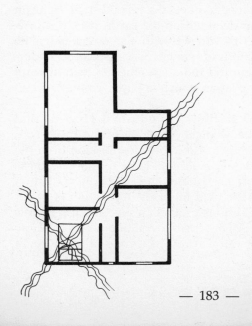
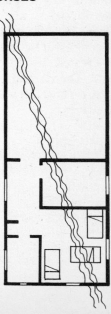

deceased victims of cancer. In many cases he even pinpointed the seat of the cancer from the exact section of the bed affected by radiation. The Central Committee for Cancer Research in Berlin published his findings and his own book describing this research is entitled *Earth Radiation, the Causative Factor in Disease and Cancer*.[2]

In Switzerland, Dr Hans Jenny carried out controlled experiments over twelve years with 24,000 mice which were tested in a radiation zone. The mice attempted to flee the affected area and when forced to live there produced lower than normal birth rates and higher infant mortality. When these mice were painted with carcinogenic coal tar they formed tumours at a much higher rate than in the control group housed in a radiation-free zone.[3]

In the 1960s, a research group from Heidelberg University and one from the Technical University in Munich teamed up to study a house in the Nechar Valley where three generations of people who slept in the same bed had all died of stomach cancer. Using scientific instruments they were able to locate the intersection of an underground watercourse and a geological fracture. Mice in wooden cages were placed over the cancer zone and their behaviour was compared with a control group of mice. The exposed mice were restless, more aggressive to the extent of devouring their young, and produced one-third the number of offspring compared with the control group.[4]

What is the explanation for this dangerous phenomenon? Some physicists and engineers have postulated that neutron radiation is generated from deep within the earth, rises upwards and is altered by coming in contact with the electromagnetic field created by the friction of water moving along underground. The normal background radiation emerges as a mixture of neutron and infra-red radiation which is partly converted into microwaves.

Russian scientists at the Institute of Industrial Hygiene and Occupational Disease at the Medical Academy of the USSR confirmed the presence and danger of microwave emission from the ground over underground watercourses. They found that these sites show ionisation changes, acoustic anomalies, gamma radiation and decreases in geomagnetic field intensity. A junction of water veins is considered to be a serious problem, especially if it travels through radioactive rocks. Super-sensitive scintillometers can now be used above water veins to measure the increased radiation at these sites.[5]

CORRECTING UNDERGROUND WATER DISTURBANCES

I had an interesting personal experience with an underground stream at the holiday property mentioned previously, north of Melbourne on the Great Dividing Range. We had been living in the place for about five years during which time I had always found it very difficult to sleep. I always awoke feeling unrefreshed and sometimes had the peculiar sensation as if my body was being pulled in a twisting direction from the bed. The house was an unusual T-shape designed by myself with cathedral type ceilings which were very high on one side. The house was built of natural materials with a pressed metal roof. I wondered if the shape of the house combined with the metal roof had produced some strange kind of energy.

At the initial Australian Vivaxis seminar held there in 1980 I complained to Fran that I was finding my Vivaxis at right angles to its proper direction. She suggested there may be a watercourse under the house and took me inside to investigate. She held her hand in the position to record a vertical flow and it moved in a circular direction over my bed and in a line straight down the house. The width of the line was about 2 metres (6 feet).

My concern at this discovery soon turned to amazement when Fran demonstrated how to treat the detrimental energy flow. She placed a tablespoon of calcium ascorbate on all the energy layers (see description of inactivating material on page 97) and sealed it in a glass jar. The jar was buried in the soil outside the window in line with the underground watercourse. We now found that the energies were completely normal throughout the whole house.

An interesting sequel took place a few years later. I had slept well in the house for some years and had almost forgotten the event when the same sleeping disturbance recurred. It occurred to me that the vitamin C powder may have become oxidised and spoilt after such a long interval. I dug up the bottle and found that the powder had become damp and yellowed. With renewed inactivator powder, the negative effect was again removed and I slept well in the house until it was sold in 1986. It was of note that the farmer next door had a large water bore which was in exact alignment with the watercourse as dowsed by Fran and myself and this suggested the existence of a substantial underground watercourse near our site.

A more scientific procedure to correct underground water disturbances is described in a German building text entitled *Do You*

Want to Live Healthily? by K.E. Lotz, a professor at a technical university in West Germany. In this experiment Lotz measured his students' skin resistance while they stood over underground water sources to indicate the disturbances induced in their bodies. An interference or dipole transmitter has been developed to use over such disturbed sites. It automatically overrides the type of microwave being emitted at any point in time. This treatment of the site is able to re-establish the normal background radiation field.[6]

Fairly recently, I had a patient whom I found was sleeping over a watercourse in a hillside suburb. She had presented with a benign throat tumour which was scheduled for surgery but she was against having an operation. At my suggestion, her bed was moved into another room and her health has since improved considerably. She is having naturopathic treatment to reduce the tumour and at the date of writing is well although the tumour has not yet disappeared.

An interesting pointer to the existence of a harmful underground stream is that ant nests are commonly found in the vicinity. Animals such as dogs, sheep, goats and cows move away from harmful areas but cats are well known for seeking out these places to sleep. In the Northern Hemisphere, forests of deciduous trees, oak and elm trees are apparently more commonly found over watercourses than other trees such as beeches or birches. To date I am not aware of any research on evergreen trees and watercourses in the Southern Hemisphere.

THE HARTMANN AND CURRY GRIDS

Geopathic stress can manifest in yet another way. Our planet has a network of criss-crossing lines which have electromagnetic properties. The Hartmann grid was discovered by Dr Ernest Hartmann and consists of lines which run north/south and east/west. It is postulated that these lines are somehow related to the magnetic properties of the North Pole. The grid lines are much closer together and more regular than ley lines. They are 2–3 metres apart (6–10 feet) and each line is 30 cm (12 inches) wide. In a similar manner to the ley lines, the width of these lines increases considerably during the full moon, with sunspot activity, and with different weather patterns.

The Curry grid was discovered by Drs Whitman and Curry following research by Curry at the Bio-Climatic Institute in southern Germany. This grid runs at a diagonal to the Hartmann grid and is also charged with electromagnetic energy. The lines are about

3.5 metres apart (11^1/$_2$ feet) This grid does not alter with the moon cycles.

There are places where the overlapping of the two grids causes a knot of energy especially if an intersection from each grid overlaps. Problems occur if someone is sleeping over an intersection of the two grids. The energy disturbance found at these points is multiplied when the charges on the grids have a similar polarity such as two negatives or two positives (see Diagram 39).

In my naturopathic practice, if I determine that someone is suffering from geopathic stress associated with these grids,

Diagram 39

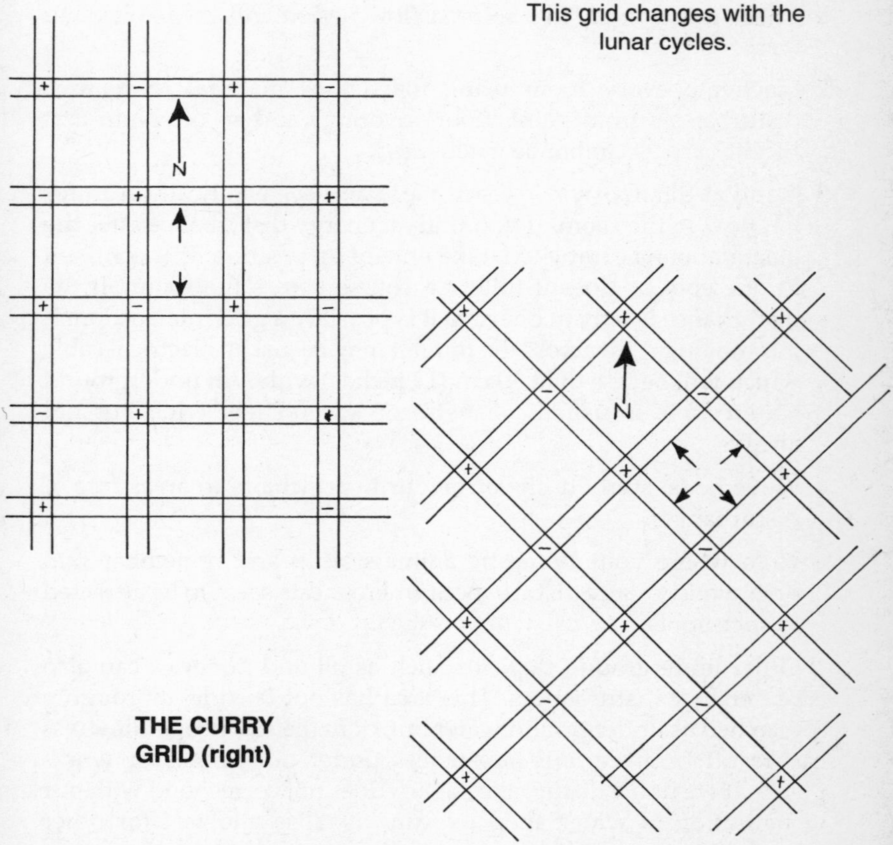

THE HARTMAN GRID

This grid changes with the lunar cycles.

THE CURRY GRID (right)

I suggest that they move the bed about one metre (3 feet). This action frequently results in improved health, particularly in terms of vitality. When I dowse for these energy disturbances on the grids, I usually find my recording hand moves in a circular motion when I focus on the disturbance. The intuitive impression I receive is of a dense knot of energy in that particular spot. You will gather that because these grid lines are fairly close together they will obviously be present in all buildings. Problems only occur when a bed or frequently-used chair is over one of the energy disturbances. The situation is further compounded if the knot of energy is over a water course.

TESTING FOR SAFE PLACES IN THE HOME

1 Check that you are in a solunar flow period and check your ion flow.

2 Inactivate every room using inactivator material to remove disturbances from paint, floor coverings and so on. Note that acrylic carpets cannot be inactivated.

3 Stand at the doorway of each room and systematically scan for ion flow in the room. If you find an energy disturbance after the inactivation is completed, take note of its position. Is it confined to one spot or does it follow a course across the room? If the disturbance is only in one area it is possibly a grid intersection. If it is moving right across the room it may be just an electrical cable which will be less than 30 cm (12 inches) wide. An underground watercourse is usually a metre or several feet wide but not always.

4 Move beds, study desks or favourite armchairs to areas free of disturbances.

5 Note where your domestic animals sleep and remember that dogs avoid energy disturbances whereas cats seem to be attracted to such spots.

Other underground deposits such as oil and minerals can also cause energy disturbances. This area has not been as thoroughly researched as underground water but, nonetheless, geopathic stress can result from various substances under our homes or workplaces. If we find a disturbance which does not correspond with our visualisation of water, then we can visualise and test for other elements.

I once conducted a Vivaxis seminar at a place called Tidbinbilla near Canberra and found disturbances in many of the rocks nearby. As I scanned the rocks, my hands moved in a circular motion, two turns one way and then two turns in the opposite way. This is an indication of radioactivity in the envionment. We had to stay well clear of the disturbance to test ourselves and teach the Vivaxis procedures. Once we become habituated to testing the health of our environment by evaluating the ion flow in an area, we become very quick at picking up abnormalities.

EARTHQUAKES, VOLCANIC ACTIVITY AND RADIATION

At a seminar I was conducting with Fran Nixon on Victoria Island, Canada, in 1983 we found that our recordings were very disturbed and we all felt very heavy in the head. Later, we received news that a volcano called Mt St Helens had violently erupted. Strong disturbances can also be recorded from earthquakes sometimes many thousands of miles away.

Testing for Earthquake Activity

The best way to test for earthquake activity is to sense the motion of your hands held at your sides while concentrating on the feet. As the period of earthquake activity approaches each hand will move in a circular motion in the opposite direction from each other. Volcanic activity will often register the same effect. Your feet are obviously sensing energy disturbance through the ground.

Observing and Testing for Radiation

Radiation can be present in the atmosphere after nuclear testing. If you find that ion flow at any time is severely disturbed it is useful to scan the sky while holding your hands by your side. Both hands will record this disturbance by moving in a circular motion first one way and then the other. Presumably underground atomic testing will produce the same response in your hands if the disturbance travels to your area.

According to the research of Fran Nixon, Force Flow 2 (the chromium vertical band) can protect against and even provide an antidote to the effects of radiation. It may be useful to know this fact if you are in a crisis situation involving radiation. My theory is that those few people who were at the centre of the Hiroshima blast and yet survived unharmed into old age may have been standing on such a layer at the time. There has been no explanation ever given for their escape from illness and injury.

THE PRACTICE OF FENG SHUI

This is an ancient Chinese science whereby a practitioner of earth energies assists people to place their houses and workplaces in the most beneficial directions and positions. They are guided by natural features of the environment such as hills, compass directions and streams. The geomancers of ancient China were aware of harmful energies and knew how to avoid problems. House design was directed along certain lines and the placement of doors, windows and furniture was considered significant in terms of positive and negative energies and to facilitate the Qi or energy flow through the dwelling.[7]

Recently, this art and science has had a big renaissance and there are many books and workshops on the subject. A friend of mine who is also a natural therapist experienced Feng Shui at first-hand. He was renting rooms in a group practice which was badly run and his practice almost disappeared. He engaged an architect familiar with Feng Shui principles to redesign a very ordinary cream brick house as a clinic. It may be coincidence, but within less than two years, the therapist concerned had as many patients again as he could handle.

The Feng Shui practitioner understands earth energies in the context of energy flow and balance both in relation to earth phenomena and man-made structures. He or she seeks to provide a healthy flow of Qi or etheric energy through each house and its environment. The placement of doors, windows, and mirrors in the house are all considered in relation to the energy flow. Outside the house, the trees and shrubs are carefully placed with the same intent in mind. The Chinese principles of Yin and Yang, or male and female energy, are applied in terms of the contours of land and buildings. Ley lines are included in the assessment and it is interesting to know ley lines have both a female and male component interlacing on various sites. This fits in with the Chinese philosophy of Yin and Yang elements in the countryside.

ELECTROMAGNETIC POLLUTION

It is only a little over a hundred years since electricity revolutionised our lives and there is probably a significant esoteric parallel to this lighting up of our planetary environment. The extent of this revolution confronts us when we fly into a large city at night and see the amazing electrification of the whole area with millions of twinkling lights far below. One hundred years is a very short time to gauge the effect of this technology on the human and animal kingdoms.

During the last twenty years many studies have been conducted on the biological and health effects of electromagnetic radiation exposure. Studies have included cell cultures exposed in the laboratory to artificially-produced fields; humans exposed similarly to electromagnetic radiation; populations exposed to environmental radiation; and groups of workers who were exposed in the course of their work.

The most controversial study in recent decades was carried out in 1979 by Wertheimer and Leeper who reported on 344 people aged 18 or less who died from cancer in Denver between 1950 and 1973.[8] The factors taken into account were electromagnetic field strength from power lines and/or transformers within 40 metres of their homes. Those who died of cancer were found to have lived in homes with higher exposure to electromagnetic radiation than the control group who were matched for ages. The study was originally rejected by government authorities but it was re-examined and found to be valid by the electrical authorities themselves.[9]

Wertheimer conducted another study in 1982 with 1,179 adults and controls who were not only matched for age and sex but also for social class. Again cancer was more likely to have occurred in homes with higher ambient electromagnetic field exposure.[10]

As part of a project by the New York Power Lines Project, studies were undertaken by Savitz on cancer in children up to the age of 14 years. Very detailed measurements were undertaken in the homes of the subjects and these measurements included all the electrical appliances. The final causal association indicated that 10–15% of all childhood cancers are attributable to magnetic fields.[11]

Apart from the likely increase of cancer after such exposure it has been found that the incidence of headache, depression and suicide is increased in persons living within about 50 metres of over-head power lines. Both electrical and magnetic fields are emitted from power lines and it is the magnetic field which is the most penetrating. One of the problems in establishing a safe distance from such lines relates to the fluctuation in the strength of the field which occurs with changing power load demands and weather conditions. There are also sudden peaks of voltage which can occur for very short times but which may have significant effects on anyone in the vicinity at the time. For instance a cable carrying 400,000 volts may sometimes carry a million volts for a millisecond.

Testing for Electromagnetic Fields

I have found that developing an understanding in this area is one of the most useful skills we can have for our home, work and travel environments. If you know how to check the normal energy flow as discussed in chapter 2, then you are equipped with this essential skill. It is a practice which can be carried out quietly without anyone noticing in many situations. When buying a new home, changing workplaces or choosing a hotel room, the ion flow can easily be checked for health-giving energies.

In the Ringwood house I lived in there were high voltage power lines about 1,000 metres further down the street. I checked the block carefully for any disturbance before our purchase. (As mentioned earlier I did not check it for ley lines!) The boundary of the electromagnetic field from the lines was just near our property boundary on a clear day. Several homes were built between our property and the power lines – one house was situated directly underneath the lines.

It was a good opportunity to investigate the phenomenon and I regularly checked the ion flow around the houses closer to the lines. At no time did I ever find a normal ion flow on these properties. It is amazing that the residents could remain in such a lifeless environment and I wonder if they felt perpetually tired. On one occasion, I had someone measure gauss strength around my home. I was interested to see whether his findings correlated with my own. He found a gauss strength well within the safety range in our home and then, for interest, he checked the house next door which was nearer the power line. His instrument measured 0.9 milli-gauss which he said was acceptable, yet in this house I had not been able to detect normal ion flow at all.

I think in this instance the human body is a more reliable instrument. For at any time and despite the many variables, it can assess the total effect on the body of the surrounding environment. I have found the extent of disturbance around the type of transformers placed in suburban streets somewhat variable but there is usually a disturbance for at least 10 metres (30 feet). In many cases this disturbance penetrates the living rooms of the home nearby.

Further Tips for Travelling

It is wise to ask for a room as far away as possible from hotel lifts and power cable conduits. The room next to a lift always contains a strong electromagnetic field. When I gave seminars in Athens I stayed regularly in a flat where my room happened to be next to the lift well. After my first stay there and a couple of disturbed nights, I realised the cause of my problem and simply slept the other way around in the bed so that only my feet were in the disturbed energy field. Over the last two decades during which I have travelled a great deal with my work, I have found that simple checking of ion flow and a discriminating choice of hotels and flats has allowed me to travel without any loss of energy and with a minimum of jet lag.

To avoid the worst of the electromagnetic field from the huge jet engines it is wise to sit in the middle block of the plane. The disturbance is minimised by the extra distance from the engines and by the buffering effect of five or six not-so-fortunate people between the seats in the middle and those near the window. As most people prefer the window and aisle seats it is always easy to obtain a seat in the middle. (The other advantage is that it is the most likely place to have a spare seat or two adjacent for lying down during long night flights.)

On arrival at my destination, I always ground myself to remove the effects of radiation from the flight. The best way to achieve balance is to locate a piece of gently sloping ground, find the energy flows, and then channel to your Vivaxis. If the hotel or place of residence has no land there is usually a public park nearby. There are a few places where this is impossible such as Bangkok.

RADIATION FROM TELEVISION AND COMPUTER SCREENS

This is a controversial area – some of the studies done on women for incidence of foetal malformation have been rejected by the authorities. But in 1988, a study of 1,583 women was conducted in Oakland, California by the Kaiser Permanent Health Group and it found serious problems. Female workers using computers for more than twenty hours per week had a forty per cent increase of miscarriage compared to a control group. Other problems include insomnia, headache, and skin rashes.[12]

My own opinion is that if you use computers every day but have a good diet and take antioxidants such as vitamins A, C and E, any negative effects will be considerably minimised. Another practical suggestion is to use a movable keyboard which can stretch back at least 45 cms (18 inches) from the screen. This reduces the electro-magnetic radiation risk to one milli-gauss. The laptop computer with its liquid crystal screen is a less dangerous alternative because it does not emit ionising radiation like the television screens of most computer terminals.

Other practical measures include installing a negative ion generator in the office to balance the constant stream of positive ions emitted by computers and air conditioning, plus having a short break every half hour away from the computer. In addition, take the antioxidant vitamins A, B complex and C and Pycnogenol® which comes from grape-seed extract to protect against the free radical effect of ionising radiation. Free radical damage involves cell membranes and can have mutagenic effects on cells.

According to medical scientist Robert Becker, all video display terminals (television sets, video games and computer monitors) emit varying amounts of radiation over a broad spectrum. Micro-waves, X-rays and ultraviolet are all emitted by these screens. If the electronic assembly of a set is poorly adjusted the terminal may emit enormous amounts of radiation. Regular maintenance and lead-impregnated glass or an acrylic screen can virtually eliminate ionising radiation but the problem of microwaves has not been solved.[13]

One of the main health problems suffered by people using com-puters every day is an increased incidence of cataracts. This may be minimised by taking the supplements of vitamin A and magnesium on a regular basis.

We need to consider the new generation of children who are introduced to computers in many of their school studies, even in primary school. These children are subjected to regular doses of electromagnetic radiation from an early age. At home, the exposure continues with the constant use of computer games and watching of television. It is important to consider the cumulative effects of the combined electromagnetic factors in the environment. For instance, does the computer operator or student constantly use a cellular phone, live in a room next to the street power lines, watch a lot of television in their spare time and have a poor diet?

In Australia about thirty per cent of people already have a cellular phone. The main problem with cellular phones is that when they are in use, the operator is receiving microwaves via the aerial held close to the brain. Exposure will obviously depend on the amount of time spent on the phone. Many parents are now buying these phones for their teenagers so that their children can keep in touch in case of emergency.

The advantages of technology in this age of communication cannot be ignored. There is no need to discard the endless possibilities for creative living which television, computers and the Internet, satellites, jet travel and cellular phones have produced. But we need to understand the health implications of such technology and to take appropriate measures to preserve health. Governments are gradually becoming alert to the health implications. There will hopefully be further appropriate legislation and controls instituted whereby power lines are kept away from residential dwellings and schools.

However, we do need to remember that the price of freedom is eternal vigilance and in this case it is freedom from health problems. The privatisation of facilities such as water and electricity poses extra problems for the general public because private organisations will not have the same accountability as government. It behoves us to be very alert to our exposure to detrimental energies as we move into the twenty-first century. On the plus side, people become more sensitive to energies they will increasingly become aware of positive energies as well as the negative energies in the environment.

SUGGESTED MENU OF EXERCISES

My hope is that people who read this book make an effort to assess all the material for themselves and gradually, in a practical way, make this material useful. Perhaps this can be done on a daily basis by following some suggestions for becoming more aware of the various energies discussed. The following menu for daily and weekly work may be adjusted to suit your individual needs and requirements.

1 Inactivate your house, car and office after checking the energies in each and note the differences afterwards. Recheck from time to time as new furniture and fittings are added (see page 97).

2 Become more aware of your environment and learn to check different environments as you travel around. Carefully check for normal ion flow around a new house or flat before you decide to move in (see page 35). Be especially careful of electrical installations nearby and make sure that the associated energy fields are checked on a clear day when they are at their maximum size.

3 Introduce the suggested safeguards for working with computers, and other equipment with electromagnetic fields (see page 193). Insist on adequate air conditioning in offices as all electrical equipment tends to saturate the atmosphere with positive ions. Old model photocopiers give off ozone which also disturbs the atmosphere.

4 Establish and mark the different force flows near your house for personal use, for inactivating pollutants in food and for energising water (see pages 67). Whenever possible place

groceries and foodstuffs for a minute or so on the phosphorus and magnesium force flows after purchase.

5 Mark a vertical band on a tree, post or wall for ease of checking both yourself and others. Ground markings have a habit of disappearing with keen lawn mowers and foul weather but are of course necessary for our own body work.

6 Regularly check yourself by standing on the force flows and at least twice per week channel to your Vivaxis on the force flow which seems most suitable on that day (see page 94).

7 When you feel your concentration or memory is poor do the exercise for the memory receptors (see page 103).

8 Repeat the carbon exercise (see page 13) after new X-rays, CAT scans and ultrasounds, and channel as soon as possible to your Vivaxis.

9 Test regularly for north and south in your environment and wherever you go on holidays (see page 14). Also be aware of the movement of the tides and your experiences with meditation at these times (see page 47).

10 Repeat the neutralising exercise (see page 18) after any medical diagnostic procedure where electrodes are placed on the body, for instance during electrocardiographs or diathermy. Women should do this exercise after electrolysis for hair removal. Assume after any surgery that you were placed in an electrical circuit for one reason or another. Become proficient at testing for foreign fields. You would also need to exercise on the energy layers and drink energised water after any anaesthesia.

11 Drink energised water at least twice per week and use the force flows regularly as general purification for water used in cooking and drinking (see page 101).

12 Practise identifying the various mineral receptors on your body and the left- and right-hand spins of the receptors in the triple groups (see page 60).

13 Begin to practise becoming aware of ley lines, underground watercourses, and the Hartmann and Curry grids and other unusual energy fields.

14 If you are a therapist, learn how to check other people's receptors and become proficient at relating health problems involving particular minerals with disturbances in people as observed on the energy bands (see page 157).

15 Regularly check your own brain receptors to monitor inter-
    ference picked up from clients (see page 117). Remember to do
    the short neutralising exercise at regular intervals during the
    day's consulting. Spend one minute inactivating the treatment
    couch after each person.

16 Please regard all this energy work as an exciting adventure
    which cannot be missed!

At the beginning of *Healing Through Earth Energies*, I said my
experience with earth energies was the most amazing adventure in
healing I had yet encountered. As I wrote the book and re-read all of
Fran Nixon's writings, I researched afresh many of the areas which
I had not explored fully before, and I was also inspired to make new
connections in our understanding about the electrical polarities of
humanity and of our earthly home. The web of life connecting us all
becomes increasingly revealed to my inner and outer sight. I rejoice
every day in these earthly insights and the opportunity to share this
living pattern with others.

NOTES

Introduction
1 Tiller, W.A., *Science and Human Transformation: Subtle Energies, Intentionality and Consciousness*, Dept of Materials Science and Engineering, Stanford University, Stanford, CA.

1 Relating to Earth as a Living Being
1 Lovelock, J.E., *Gaia - A New Look at Life on Earth*, Oxford Press, New York 1979.
2 Bailey, A.A., *A Treatise on Cosmic Fire*, Lucis Press, London, 1952.
3 Wilbur, K., *Up From Eden*, Shambhala, Boulder, 1983.
4 Laszlo, G., *The Creative Cosmos – A Unified Science of Matter, Life and Mind*, Floris Books, Edinburgh 1993.
5 Briggs, J.P. and Peate, F.D., *Looking Glass Universe*, Fontana Books, Great Britain, 1985.
6 Jacka, J., *Meditation, The Most Natural Therapy*, Lothian, Melbourne, 1990.
7 Bailey, A.A., *Esoteric Astrology*, Lucis Press, London, 1951.
8 Nixon, F., *Born to be Magnetic*, Vol. 1., p.13, Magnetic Publishers, British Columbia, 1971
9 Bentov I., *Stalking the Wild Pendulum*, Wildwood House, Great Britain, 1978.
10 Becker, R., *Cross Currents*, Jeremy Tarcher, Los Angeles, 1990.
11 Becker, R. ibid p.74.
12 Baker, R.R., 'Human Magnetor-reception for Navigation,' *Electromagnetic Fields and Neuromagnetic Function*, Ed. M.E.O'Connor and R.H. Levely, Alan R. Liss, New York, 1988.
13 Nixon, F., *Search For Vivaxis* , Part 1, Magnetic Publishers, British Columbia, 1982.

2 Planetary Vibrations and Frequencies
1 Tansley, D., *Dimensions of Radionics*, Health Science Press, Devon, 1977.
2 Baker, R.R., *Nature*, No. 301, 1988.
3 Jacka, J., *Frontiers of Natural Therapy*, Lothian, Melbourne, 1989.
4 Laszlo, E., *The Creative Cosmos*, Floris Books, Edinburgh, 1993.
5 Briggs, J.P. and Peat, F.D., *Looking Glass Universe*, Fontana Books, Great Britain, 1985.
6 Burr, H.S., *Blueprint For Immortality*, Neville Spearman, London, 1972.
7 Bailey, A.A., *Esoteric Healing*, Lucis Press, London, 1953.
8 Goldman, J., *Healing Sounds*, Element Books, Dorset, 1992.

9 Tomatis, A., *The Conscious Ear*, Station Hill Press, New York, 1991.
10 Andrews, T., *Sacred Sounds*, Llewellyn Publications, Minnesota, 1992.
11 Nixon, F., *Search For Vivaxis* , Part 1, Magnetic Publishers, British Columbia, 1982.
12 Bentov, I., *Stalking the Wild Pendulum*, Wildwood House, Great Britain, 1978.

3 Planetary Cycles and Rhythms
1 Gauquelin, M., *Cosmic Influences on Human Behaviour*, ASI Publishers, New York, 1978.
2 Gauquelin, M., *Birth Times - A Scientific Investigation of the Secrets of Astrology*, Hill and Yang, New York, 1983.
3 Sandyk, R. et al, 'Magnetic Fields and Seasonality of Affective Illness: Implications for Therapy, *Int. J. Neuroscience*, 58(3-4):261-7 June 1991.
4 Watson, L., *Supernature* Coronet Books, London 1973.
5 Bailey, A.A., *Esoteric Astrology*, Lucis Press, London, 1951.
6 Bailey, A.A., *Esoteric Psychology*, Lucis Press, London, 1942.
7 Burr, H.S., *Blueprint for Immortality*, Neville Spearman, London, 1972.
8 Brown, F.A., 'Persistent Activity Rhythms in the Oyster' *American Journal of Physiology*,178:510, 1954.
9 Nixon, F., *Search for Vivaxis* , Part 1, Revised Ed. Magnetic Publishers, British Columbia, 1982.

4 The Vibratory Dance of the Elements
1 Nixon, F., *Search For Vivaxis* , Part 1, Revised Ed. p.18. Magnetic Publishers, British Columbia, 1982.
2 Nixon, F., *Born To Be Magnetic*, Vol. 1, p.108. Magnetic Publishers, British Columbia, 1971.
3 Nixon, F., *Search For Vivaxis*, Part 1, Revised. Ed. p.50. Magnetic Publishers, British Columbia, 1982.
4 Nixon, F., *Search For Vivaxis*, Part 2, p.22. Magnetic Publishers, British Columbia. 1979
5 Nixon, F., ibid p.40.
6 Nixon, F. and Parminter, I., *Vivaxis Beams*, Magnetic Publishers, British Columbia, 1980.

5 The Vivaxis Connection
1 Nixon, F., *Born to Be Magnetic*, Vol. 1, p.13. Magnetic Publishers, British Columbia, 1971.
2 Nixon, F., *Born to Be Magnetic*, Vol.1, p.30 & 108, Magnetic Publishers, British Columbia,1971.
3 Nixon, F., *Born to be Magnetic*, Vol. 2, p.91, Magnetic Publishers, British Columbia, 1973
4 Becker, R. and Marino, A., *Electromagnetism and Life*, p.30. State University of New York, New York, 1982.
5 Nixon, F., *Born to Be Magnetic*, Vol. 1, p.46 & 90. Magnetic Publishers, British Columbia, 1971.
6 Bailey, A.A., *Esoteric Healing*, Lucis Press, London, 1953
7 Jacka, J., *Frontiers of Natural Therapy*, Lothian, Melbourne, 1989.
8 Oldfield, H. & Coghill, R., *The Dark Side of the Brain*, Element, Dorset, 1988.
9 Nixon, F., *Born to Be Magnetic*, Vol.1, p.32, Magnetic Publishers, British Columbia, 1971.
10 Nixon, F., *Search For Vivaxis*, Part 2, p.24. Magnetic Publishers, British Columbia, 1979.

6 Using the Vivaxis and Energy Layers
1 Nixon, F., *Born to Be Magnetic*, Vol. 1, p.79, Magnetic Publishers, British Columbia, 1971.

2 Nixon, F., *Search for Vivaxis*, Part 1, p.13 Revised Ed. Magnetic Publishers, British Columbia, 1982.
3 Nixon, F., *Search For Vivaxis*, Part 1, p.25. Revised Ed. Magnetic Publishers, British Columbia, 1982.
4 Goodrich, J., *Natural Vision*, Greenhouse Publications, Richmond, Australia, 1985.
5 Nixon, F., *Search For Vivaxis*, Part 1, p.54. Revised Ed. Magnetic Publishers, British Columbia, 1982.
6 Nixon, F., *Born To Be Magnetic*, Vol. 2, p.118. Magnetic Publishers, British Columbia, 1973.

7 Testing our Energy Receptors
1 Nixon, F., *Born To Be Magnetic*, Vol.1, p.112. Magnetic Publishers, British Columbia. 1971.
2 Nixon, F., ibid Vol. 1, p.43
3 Nixon, F., Manual, Part 2, p.31, Magnetic Publishers, British Columbia, 1974.
4 Nixon, F., *Born to be Magnetic*, Vol. 1, p.121, Magnetic Publishers, British Columbia, 1971.
5 Nixon, F., ibid p.113.
6 Nixon, F., ibid p.128.
7 Nixon, F., *Born to be Magnetic*, Vol 2, p.30. Magnetic Publishers, 1973.
8 Nixon, F., *Born to be Magnetic*, Vol. 1, p.150

8 Glands Chakras and Force Flows
1 Bailey, A.A., *Esoteric Healing*, Lucis Trust, London, 1953.
2 Hall, R.S. et al., 'Transformation of the Personality and the Immune System,' *Advances* Vol. 10, No. 4.1994, 7-15.
3 Jacka, J., *Meditation, The Most Natural Therapy*, Lothian, Melbourne, 1990.
4 Jacka, J., *A-Z of Natural Therapies*, Lothian, Melbourne, 1987.
5 McLaughlin, C. and Davidson, G., *Spiritual Politics*, Ballantyne Books, New York, 1994.
6 Moynihan, J., 'Stress-induced Modulation of Immunity: Animal Models and Human Implications, *Advances: Journal of Mind-Body Health*, Vol. 10, 4, Fall 1994.
7 Bailey, A.A., *A Treatise on Cosmic Fire*, p.98, Lucis Press, London. 1952.

9 The White Flows and Head Chakras
1 Becker, R., *Cross Currents*, p.76. Jeremy Tarcher, Los Angeles, 1990.
2 Sandyk, R. et al., 'Magnetic Fields and Seasonality of Affective Fields: Implications for Therapy,' *International Journal of Neuro Science*, 58 (3-4) 1991, 261-7.
3 Maestroni, G.J., 'The Immunoneuroendocrine Role of Melatonin,' *J. of Pineal Research*, 14, (1) Jan. 1993, 1-10.
4 Jacka, J., *Meditation, The Most Natural Therapy*, Lothian, 1990.
5 Nixon, F., *Environmental Force Flows Stimulating the Pineal Gland*, Magnetic Publishers, British Columbia, 1983.

10 Diagnosing and Correcting Disturbances
1 Nixon, F., *Search For Vivaxis*, Part 1, p.56. Revised ed. Magnetic Publishers, British Columbia, 1982.
2 Nixon, F., *Supplement to Vivaxis Beams: Force Flow X*, Magnetic Publishers, British Columbia, 1982.
3 Nixon, F., *Search For Vivaxis*, Part 2, Magnetic Publishers, British Columbia, 1979.

11 Earth Phenomena Which Affect our Lives
1 Watkins, A., *The Old Straight Track*, Abacus, London, 1974.
2 Devereux, P., *Places of Power*, Blandford, London, 1990.
3 Heselton, P., *Earth Mysteries*, Element, Dorset, 1991.
4 Lonegren, Sig (Compiler), *The Dowsing Rod Kit*, Lothian, Melbourne, 1995.

5 Miller, H. and Broadbent, P. ,*The Sun and the Serpent*, Pendradragon Press, Cornwall, 1989.
6 Cathie, B., *Harmonic 33*, A.H. & A.W. Reed, London, 1968 and *Harmonic 695*, A.H. & A.W. Reed, London, 1971.
7 Bailey, A.A. *Destiny of the Nations*, Lucis Press, London, 1949.
8 *Nikola Tesla: Letters, Patents, Articles,* Published by Nikola Tesla Museum, Beograd, 1956.
9 Nixon, F. *Search For Vivaxis*, Part 2, p.14. Magnetic Publishers, British Columbia, 1979.

12 Harmful Earth Energies and Geopathic Stress

1 Moore, A., 'Are You Under Geopathic Stress,' *Australian Wellbeing*, No. 15, 1986.
2 Von Pohl, G.F., *Earth Radiation the Causative Factor in Disease and Cancer*, Fortschritt fuer Alle, Feucht, W.Germany, 1932
3 Kopp, J.A., 'Healthy Living By Elimination of Soil Influences Detrimental to Health,' *J. of Swiss Society for Housing (das Wohnen)* No. 11. 1970
4 McCreary, J.B., 'Water Theory,' *The American Dowser Quarterly*, Nov. 1981, p.22.
5 Kopp, J.A., 'On the Physics of Geopathogenic Phenomenon,' *J. for Practical Medicine*, Heidelberg, May 1. 71.
6 Lotz, K.E., *Do You Want To Live Healthily?*, Paffrath-Druck KG, Remscheid, 1982.
7 Eitel, E., *Feng-Shui, The Science of Sacred landscape in Old China*, Synergetic press, London, 1984.
8 Wertheimer, N. and Leeper, E., 'Electrical Wiring Configuration and Childhood Cancer,' *J of Epidemiol*, 111, 1980, 273-284.
9 New York State Power Lines Project, *Biological Effects of Power Line Fields*. New York, US Dept. of Health, 1987.
10 Wertheimer N., & Leeper, E., 'Adult Cancer Related To Electrical Wires Near The Home,' *J. of Epedemiol*. 11 (4), 1982, 345-355.
11 Savitz D.A., 'Childhood Cancer and Electromagnetic Field Exposure,' Report to the New York State Department of Health, Power Lines Project, New York, US Dept. of Health, 1987.
12 Dowsen, D.I., 'A Review of Epidemiological Studies into the Health Effects of Electromagnetic Fields, *Complementary Medical Research*, Vol. 3, No. 2, 1989.
13 Becker, R., *Cross Currents*, Jeremy Tarcher, Los Angeles, 1990, p.276.

GLOSSARY

Areahola forces a force of light waves coming from north and south which can be harnessed via sea salt and soda to promote health and balance.

astral energies associated with our feelings and psychic activities such as clairvoyance and clairaudience. The astral body is our vehicle for emotional expression.

aura fields of energy which surround and originate from a human being or animal. The aura may include etheric, astral or emotional, mental and spiritual energies.

brain receptor a point on the skull which receives and transmits energy.

chakras the energy centres in the human or animal energy field.

Curry grid an energy grid which covers the surface of the earth in lines diagonal to those of the Hartmann grid. It is electro-magnetically charged. The lines are about 3.5 metres (11^1/$_2$ feet) apart.

dowsing a method of searching for water or minerals with a divining rod.

etheric energy a common name given to the energy which underlies all physical bodies. It is the vital factor in health and disease.

etheric body the vehicle for the etheric energy of plants, animals or humans. It provides the pattern or blueprint for growth and regrowth.

energy layers or bands successive layers of energy around the earth. They are arranged like the skins of an onion but each layer separated by 3–4 metres (8–12 feet).

force flows energy flows carried by the energy layers of the earth. The Vivaxis flows are comprised of frequencies for all the life-giving elements. There are also some naturally-occurring and man-made detrimental force flows.

geopathic stress areas of pathology in the earth such as underground watercourses and oil deposits which can have injurious effects on our health. The term is also often used to cover man-made earth sickness such as occurs from power lines.

gravitational force flow and elements a force flow carrying frequencies which are associated with the gravitational forces of the sun and moon. This force flow is also associated with the gravitational layer of our energy field or aura and with our Vivaxis.

Hartmann grid a global energy grid identified by Dr Ernest Hartmann with lines which run north/south and east/west. The lines are 2–3 metres (6–10 feet) apart.

ion flow the flow of negative and positive ions in the body which gives a basic indication of flow in the energy field.

inactivation removal of chaotic energies from our environment.

Kirlian photography a photograph or light image produced by placing a person in a high frequency field.

ley line a track on the surface of the earth which is understood to carry energy from one place to another. Ley lines form a grid with lines about 2 km (one mile) apart.

magnetic elements and force flows force flows carrying the frequencies for elements such as iron, copper, silver, gold, nickel and selenium. These force flows are also associated with the magnetic layer of our energy field or aura.

major period the period of a high tide which lasts for about one and a half hours.

minor period the period of a low tide which lasts for about twenty minutes.

radiesthetic sense the ability to perceive extra-sensory energies.

radionics the practice of energy healing from a distance using an instrument which transmits the frequencies which can correct disease patterns. A photograph, blood spot or sample of hair from the subject is used to make a diagnosis.

receptors tiny energy transmitters on the surface of the body similar to acupuncture points. They are associated with particular mineral frequencies.

solunar flow the period of about six hours between high and low tides.

vector a line representing force or velocity.

vegatest a patented electronic device used to measure skin resistance.

Vivaxis the sphere of energy which connects our energy field to that of the earth. It is established in the last few weeks before birth and remains in the same position throughout our life. The Vivaxis flow contains magnetic and gravitational forces which influence our health and well-being.

INDEX